AN INTRODUCTION TO
MATHEMATICAL LOGIC

PRENTICE-HALL INTERNATIONAL, INC., *London*
PRENTICE-HALL OF AUSTRALIA, PTY. LTD., *Sydney*
PRENTICE-HALL OF CANADA, LTD., *Toronto*
PRENTICE-HALL OF INDIA PRIVATE LTD., *New Delhi*
PRENTICE-HALL OF JAPAN, INC., *Tokyo*

AN INTRODUCTION TO
MATHEMATICAL LOGIC

GERSON B. ROBISON

Department of Mathematics
The State University of New York
New Paltz, New York

PRENTICE-HALL, INC., *Englewood Cliffs, N.J.*

Current printing (last digit):

10 9 8 7 6 5 4 3 2 1

Library of Congress Catalog Card Number: 69-14806

Printed in the United States of America

To John and Judy
         who have read this book
and to Virginia
         who reads me

PREFACE

This text was developed for a course at the upper-sophomore or junior level within the mathematics curriculum. It is intended as a course in logic useful to the student of mathematics rather than as a beginning course for a prospective specialist in philosophy. I have no doubt that the sophisticated reader will find sins of omission and commission in this presentation—no text is entirely satisfactory to anyone, its author included. Most of the sins, I hope, will have resulted from deliberate choices of what I considered the lesser evil in the light of the aims of the text. One notable example is the omission of any discussion of language levels or of the distinction between use and mention of a symbol. In some places quotation marks are used to emphasize that a symbol is mentioned, but consistency in that usage was abandoned after the first draft, because it frequently turned out to have a distracting influence instead of a clarifying one.

With the exception of a few dispensable examples from the elementary calculus, a background in high school mathematics is all that is actually drawn upon. With a reasonably capable class, the whole text can be covered in a standard three semester-hour course. The plan of the book is described in § 1-7 (to thwart the student who habitually skips prefaces), and the reader might do well to turn to it at this point.

The following comments may be helpful in planning variants:

Chapter 1 is mainly for motivation and orientation. It need not take more than one class session. In Chapters 2 through 5 the foundations are laid. Sections 3-7 and 5-10 can be omitted or lightly treated, but the rest should be presented and deliberately paced. Competence in a new language takes time. The details of the proofs in Chapter 6 may be slid over, but close study should be given to what the theorems mean and how they are used. The theorems in this chapter are frequently referred to later. Chapters 7 and 8 should be covered in detail through § 8-4. The main aim of this book is reached with the definition of "formal proof." The rest is application, and the instructor may prefer other examples. Chapter 9 is brief, and in my opinion, pays off well in usefulness to the student. Chapters 10 and 11 provide a bridge to less formal methods, and, of course, deal with matters fundamental to all modern mathematics.

As usual, I can give only a partial list of my creditors:

Mr. A. Rittenberg, for encouraging me to get started fifteen years ago.

Dr. E. Nauss for early and cogent criticisms.

Professor Joel Pitt, who has used a preliminary edition in his classes, and with whom I have had many helpful discussions.

The students who served as guinea pigs, particulary those who asked embarrassing questions.

Mrs. W. Steffens, for typing assistance.

There are many writers and teachers to whom I am indebted in some degree, for examples of both what to do and what not to do. My greatest debt in this regard, entirely in the positive sense, is to Professor J. Barkley Rosser, from whom I first heard of the intricacies of Rules G and C.

Finally, especial thanks are due to Professor Bruce Meserve. As the primary editor of this text for Prentice-Hall, he rescued my manuscript from obscurity in more than one way.

Gerson B. Robison

CONTENTS

CAST OF CHARACTERS IN THE ORDER OF THEIR APPEARANCE

$\sim$	12	$\vdash$	65
$\wedge$	12	$\widehat{x}$	75
$\vee$	13	$\rightarrow$	75
$\Rightarrow$	13	R	86
$\Leftrightarrow$	15	$\mathfrak{D}$	92
[,]	15		
$\underline{\vee}$	24	$\lceil$	98
$\mid$	40		
$*$	41, 121†	————	101
$\exists x$	42	$\forall Z$	111
$\forall x$	42	$\varphi(\alpha)$	143
$\forall xy$	43	$\in$	152
$\exists xy$	43	$\notin$	151, 169†
α	52	b' (set-comp.)	154, 170†
β	52	$\cup$	154, 168†
$P(x)$	57	$\cap$	154, 168†
$\exists_1 x$	60	$\subseteq$	155, 170†
$P(x)$—$P(y)$	61	$\notin$	155
$P(x)$—$P(\alpha)$	61	$\neq$	155
$P(\alpha)$—$P(\beta)$	62	$\nsubseteq$	155
$P(x, y)$—$P(w, t)$	64	$\varnothing$	157, 169†

† Dual role.

Chapter 1

MATHEMATICS AND REALITY

1-1 ABSTRACT OR APPLIED

Mathematics has two aspects, each with its own fascination and beauty. One is that of abstract mathematics, of mathematics in itself, an apparently self-contained creation of the human mind; the other is that of applied mathematics, mathematics in the world, reacting to and reacting upon human activity everywhere. Between them there is a two-way flow of communication, of concrete problems looking for theoretical formulation and of theory looking for concrete application.

We shall be concerned almost entirely with the first aspect, but not because of any conviction that it is more important. It is rather that, except on the most elementary levels, applied mathematics is for the specialists. Moreover, for an *understanding* of applied mathematics, an understanding of mathematical theory of an appropriate kind is a prerequisite.

If you should ask a random collection of people what the outstanding characteristic of mathematics might be, you would get a variety of answers, such as "frequent definitions," "use of numbers," and so on. But if your collection included a modern mathematician, he would unhesitatingly choose "logical structure." Number relations take second place; although there is no mathematics without a heavy dependence upon logic, there are some advanced branches of mathematics in which the notion of number occurs in only a primitive way, almost at the "one, two, many" level of some scientifically naive cultures. In lattice theory, for example, the only number ideas directly involved to any great extent are "none," "one," "two," "finitely many," and "infinitely many."

The first typical mathematical system that a student usually meets is that of Euclidean geometry. (It *is* typical, in spite of its well-known flaws as traditionally presented.) If his experience has been limited, he may have the impression that axioms, theorems, and proofs are peculiar to geometry, and exceptional in mathematics as a whole. But if his experience has been wider and deeper, he should have learned that the real exception is the sort of goings-on generally found in the elementary arithmetic and algebra courses. Whether they deserve the name "mathematics" at all is questionable, since they frequently lack any pretense of a theoretical basis. Some degree of theory is necessary for good applied mathematics at every level.

I-2 DEFINITIONS AND UNDEFINED EXPRESSIONS

Even before the usual introduction to formal mathematics in the tenth year, the student has probably been impressed by the ubiquitous occurrence of definitions in mathematical study. It seems that everything in mathematics has to be defined. It should be obvious, however, that any attempt to do so will end in a futile circularity. For instance, mathematics itself may be defined as "The characteristic activity of mathematicians." Ah, but what is a mathematician? Clearly, a mathematician is "one who is active in mathematics." Taken together, these two definitions do not define anything. If we use them as our sole criteria, any occupation, together with its practitioners, will pass the test.

A way out is to leave "mathematician" undefined, and to proceed on the assumption that we can recognize one by his own declaration, or by his peculiar gait and his nearsighted vision. Then, by observing his "characteristic activity" (?), we may obtain an idea of what "mathematics" means.

Explicit recognition that some words or phrases should be left undefined in a logical system is of relatively recent origin. Such words fall into two broad classes. The first of these is the common coin of the language: words such as "and," "if," "then," "every," and so on. They are left undefined, but it is assumed that the reader is familiar with their meanings and uses. Even then, one needs occasionally to straighten out possible ambiguities. The second class of undefined expressions forms the basis of the technical vocabulary; such words and phrases as "point," "line," "number," "is an element of," and the like. Whereas the expressions of the first class may be understood to have a unique meaning, *those of the second class are held to be free of any intrinsic meaning*, so that the word "point," for example, may have different interpretations in different applications of the same system. *There must be an explicit listing of the undefined technical expressions that will be used in a given system*, and all other technical expressions must be defined in terms of these or other previously defined expressions.

EXERCISES

1. Explain the sentence in § 1-2: "If we use them as our sole criteria, any occupation, together with its practitioners, will pass the test."

2. Choose a word at random in a dictionary. Look up the principal terms in its definition. (Avoid mere synonyms.) Repeat the process for these terms, carrying on until you cross your own trail, not necessarily at the beginning. (A dictionary is not expected to be a logical system.)

3. Consider the following definitions as a pair:
(1) A mathematician is a person whose name is listed in the current *Combined Membership List of the AMS, MAA, and SIAM.*
(2) Mathematics is the characteristic activity of mathematicians.
Discuss this pair of definitions from

(a) A logical standpoint.
(b) A psychological standpoint.
(c) A practical standpoint.

4. "A common word has definite meaning only in context." Explain this statement, using "fast" as an illustration.

5. See if you can find a reasonably common word for which the statement in Exercise 4 is false. If not, discuss two of the words you tried out.

1-3 UNPROVED STATEMENTS

It is just as futile to try to prove all statements by formal deduction as it is to try to define all terms. There must be a collection of statements that we do not prove, to serve as a starting point, and, just as with the undefined expressions, these statements must be explicitly listed. You know them as the "axioms" or "postulates" of the system. (Although distinctions have been made by some writers between "axiom" and "postulate," we shall follow modern usage and treat these words as synonyms.) Perhaps you were told that they were statements that were "obviously true" or "self-evident." If so, your teacher was worse than old-fashioned, he was obsolete. If he called them "statements assumed to be true," he was somewhat nearer the mark. If he identified the postulates simply as permissible statements, then he was, in that respect at least, a modern mathematician.

It is probable that Euclid believed his axioms to represent true statements about the physical world, and they were accepted as such well into the nineteenth century. But in the latter half of that century, a new evaluation of the role of the postulates and, indeed, of mathematics itself, began to take shape. In this modern viewpoint, the statements of a mathematical system, postulated or proved, are not true or false in any sense of physical or other observable reality. In particular, the axioms are just a *specified* collection of formal statements that are not to be proved and that may be used in formal proofs of other statements of the system. There is more than mere analogy here with the collection of undefined terms; the two notions actually complement each other. In a sense, the postulates define the undefined terms.

If this were all of the modern viewpoint, mathematics would have indeed degenerated into "a game played according to certain rules with meaningless marks on paper."† However, I doubt whether any mathematician would seriously equate the social significance of his field with that of the chess or bridge expert. What mathematician would not be contemptuous of a liberal arts college that did not offer a respectable course in mathematics? Is there a mathematician who does not believe total ignorance of mathematics to be a serious intellectual defect?

It is the well-known success with which its structures have been applied to problems in the concrete world that has made mathematics a "required course" today. Now, how can there be any connection between the real world and a collection of meaningless statements phrased in meaningless words? If there is no truth or falsity in a mathematical system, how do we use it to discover truth in the world about us?

I-4 MODELS AND INTERPRETATIONS

The connection lies in the concepts of "model" and "interpretation." For example, let us start with the mathematical statement "$2 \times 5 = 10$." To the mathematician, the equality is a formal statement that can be deduced from the postulates and definitions of certain mathematical systems. There are also other systems in which it is possible to disprove it, and still others in which it is not even meaningful. (See Exercises 1 and 2 of § 1-6.) Now consider a travel agent who is booking tourists from Hyar to Thar by way of

† A Formalist definition offered by D. Hilbert (1862–1943).

Yonda. There are two ways to go from Hyar to Yonda, and five ways to go from Yonda to Thar. In one of the systems in which $2 \times 5 = 10$ is provable, the undefined expressions of the system (including $\times$) can be assigned meanings so that the axioms become meaningful and true statements with respect to the travel agent's physical situation. Under such an assignment of meanings, or **interpretation**, the mathematical statement then tells us that there are ten possible routes from Hyar to Thar by way of Yonda.

The mathematician who is trying the power or testing the consistency of his system may say, "I have found a concrete model of my system." On the other hand, the travel agent technician may say, "I have found a mathematical model of the concrete situation." In either case, every relevant postulate must be checked to see whether it is in fact a true statement under the given interpretation, and every relevant definition must be scrutinized to determine just what the defined expression now represents.

Let us now look at another technician. He has surveyed a rectangular portion of the earth near the equator, and found it to be 2 miles wide from east to west and 5 miles long from north to south. Since $2 \times 5 = 10$, he concludes that the area of the plot is 10 square miles. Actually, his mathematical model is not the same as that of the travel agent, and has a different set of postulates, involving geometry, measure theory, and the properties of the real number system. However, in that model $2 \times 5 = 10$ is still provable, and he is confident that his choice of model makes his result a truthful one.

There is a question that now clamors for consideration: How can you be sure that your abstract postulates have been transformed into true statements by a particular interpretation? Is it not possible that the mathematical model has not been well chosen, and that, owing to faulty observation, interpreted statements that are actually false have been checked in as true?

This unfortunate situation is not only possible, it is probable in many fields. An outstanding example may be found in modern physics. Up to the dawn of the twentieth century, a generation after the *logical* possibility of non-Euclidean geometries had been accepted by mathematicians, there was little doubt on the part of physicists as to the accuracy of Eucildean geometry as a model for physical space. Today, particularly in those branches concerned with stellar distances and magnitudes, a non-Euclidean geometry may turn out to be more suitable. In mathematizing the social sciences, the first models chosen were those inspired by the needs of the physical sciences. Today some investigators feel that more suitable models might be found in other parts of mathematics. Game theory, a relatively new branch of mathematics, is, at least in part, a result of the search for mathematical models better suited to social problems.

The demand for truthfulness in the interpretation is thus necessarily qualified by the phrase "within the limits of possible accuracy of observation," and even that demand can be weakened. The reader with a knowledge of the geometry of spherical surfaces knows that the area is not 10 square miles in the surveyor's problem. In fact, if a region on a spherical surface is bounded by four geodesics (shortest paths), it cannot have right angles at all four corners. However, the error in a region of the size and at the locality described would, in most cases, be of no practical significance. (The error grows significantly large near the poles.) So the surveyor is only interested in truth within *desired* limits of accuracy.

This is a good place to turn back from our very sketchy foray into the relation between abstract mathematics and reality. Very thorny thickets lie ahead, and the greatest minds have not been able to agree on a safe path. But before we do leave this area, let us point out a tremendous consequence of using terms without intrinsic meaning and statements without intrinsic truth or falsity. It is this: *The same mathematical system can serve as a model for many different concrete situations.* To the extent of our confidence in the truth of our interpreted postulates, we may be confident of the truth of our interpreted theorems.

I-5 WHERE DO LITTLE AXIOMS COME FROM?

Part of the answer to this question has already been suggested. Euclid's postulates were a selected list of statements about physical space that were considered to be true; from them all known space relations were to be derived and others discovered. Newton added basic "truths" about force and motion to Euclid's system, and derived the laws of dynamics found in *Principia*.† Almost a century later, we can hear an echo of these formulations in the resounding words of the Declaration of Independence.

Concrete situations still provide a source of mathematical systems. The modern twist to this process is that when the postulates suggested by the reality have been written out, they are then permitted to bud off as an independent, abstract system. This may be done even before they form a completely satisfactory model of the system from which they derive. Game theory, for example, is still a long way from solving the problems that suggested its structure.

† See the lecture on Newton by E. N. Da C. Andrade, included in *The World of Mathematics*, J. Newman, Ed. (New York: Simon and Schuster, 1956), pp. 255–276.

A more inbred kind of system generating is to alter one or more postulates in an established system. It was in this manner that non-Euclidean geometries came into being, more than half a century before there was any external demand for them. Similarly, the curiosity about possible systems in which $x(yz)$ did not always equal $(xy)z$ allowed algebraists to initiate what is today one of the more active fields of mathematical research.

It is not necessary to alter a postulate to derive a new system from an old one. One can drop or add entire postulates. Conceivably, one might set down an arbitrary list of undefined expressions and several random statements about them for postulates, but, as far as I know, no one has ever succeeded in creating a viable mathematical system that way. The likelihood that such a system would be both nontrivial and consistent (free of contradiction) is extremely small.

1-6 MATHEMATICAL SYSTEMS

Since we shall be discussing mathematical systems, let us try to clarify what is meant by that expression. By a **mathematical system** Σ we shall mean the following three-part structure:

(1) A list of undefined symbols

These symbols are used in a variety of ways. Some, such as individual letters and numerals, represent objects of the system. Others, such as the operation symbols of arithmetic, may be used to build more complex terms. Still others, such as $=$ and $\subseteq$, express relations and serve grammatically as verbs. A fourth group of symbols, which will be of particular concern to us, are those which serve as connectives or as modifiers of whole statements. This group will be discussed in detail in Chapters 2, 3, and 4. Informally, many words of ordinary discourse, such as "is," "belongs," and "greater," are usually permitted; in a formal system it is possible to dispense with such words. It is true that we may still have to verbalize the symbols when speaking. We may *write* $\forall x[x^2 > z]$, but we must *say* "For every ex, ex squared is greater than zee."

(2) A set of rules for determining which (finite) strings of symbols qualify as statements

Any statement formed in accord with these rules is called a "statement of the system" or a "statement of Σ," whether it is provable, disprovable, or undecided. Certain provable ones are called "theorems."

(3) A list of postulates

These must qualify as statements according to the rules. Along with the postulates we can include definitions, subject to special restrictions that are discussed in Chapter 10.

I-7 THE PLAN OF THIS BOOK

By this point in your mathematical life, you have surely been convinced of the nontriviality of the task of finding a valid proof. The problem can be separated into two aspects. The first is: How may a proof be found? and the second is: How can its validity be checked? This book will deal with the latter question, but not because the former one is any less important to the mathematician or to the teacher. The question of how to find a proof must be answered largely in terms of analogy and psychological insight. We try to repeat our own successful approaches in similar settings, and encourage our students to do likewise. For an examination of the role of intuition and insight in attacking mathematical problems, the works of G. Polya are highly instructive. There is also the well-known essay on the subject by J. Hadamard.†

To obtain a really close approximation of a complete answer to the second question has been one of the main achievements of modern symbolic logic. This has been done by making liberal use of abstraction and formalism to reduce dependence on meaning to a vanishing point. The absence of dependence on meaning makes it possible to direct one's attention to the mechanics of what can be done with given strings of symbols to obtain a desired conclusion. We can then provide a set of rules specifying precisely what may be done in the way of formal manipulation with such strings. We need not worry about such questions as: *What does "$x > y$" stand for?* or *What is the real meaning of an imaginary number?* It is sufficient to check that the *rules* have been followed. The rules are even such that one does not have to be a logician to see that they have been obeyed, but merely a competent clerk. In Chapter 5 we shall present a set of such rules, together with a description of the arrangement of one's work in applying those rules (the *demonstration*).

These rules must discuss certain *kinds* of statements, rather than the statements themselves. It is therefore necessary to develop a symbolism that can

† G. Polya, *How to Solve It* (New York: Doubleday, 1957); *Mathematics and Plausible Reasoning* (Princeton, N.J.: Princeton University Press, 1954); *Mathematical Discovery* (New York: Wiley, 1965).

J. Hadamard, *The Psychology of Invention in the Mathematical Field* (Princeton, N.J.: Princeton University Press, 1945).

display some amount of the internal *structure* of a statement without being more specific about its *content*. Chapters 2, 3 and 4 are devoted to that purpose.

Since the rules of formal logic are not themselves subject to formal proof, they must be of a nature that makes them virtually unassailable from an intuitive standpoint. Hence the list in Chapter 5 is short (there are just ten rules), and each rule deals with a very limited manipulation. As a result, any proof constructed in exact accordance with those rules would be impractically long for any but the most trivial theorems, as the illustrative examples in Chapter 5 show. In Chapters 6, 7, and 8, additional rules are introduced which permit much shorter proofs. These rules are based strictly on the rules of Chapter 5. For each proof obtained by allowing the more sophisticated rules of Chapters 6, 7, and 8, there is a proof using only the rules of Chapter 5.

Chapter 9 is a short detour into a matter of technique, and in Chapter 10 a loose end left over from the avowed formalism of Chapters 2 through 5 is woven back into the fabric.

Finally, Chapters 11 and 12 offer an opportunity to apply the logical system to set theory, a part of mathematics that lies next to logic itself as a basis for all other mathematical theory as it is presented today. In these last two chapters, much more informal methods of proof will be permitted, while keeping clear the connection between these informal methods and the formalities of the preceding chapters. Thus, at least in concept, one would be able to replace any informal proof with a Chapter 5 "demonstration."

This approach will show that we do not need a multitude of independent rules to provide for each kind of process found in informal, colloquial logic. Instead, our logical processes can be ultimately founded upon a short set of rather exact rules, the 10 rules of Chapter 5.

EXERCISES

1. Can you find a mathematical system in which "$2 \times 5 = 10$" is meaningful, but false? Look into numeration systems in recent arithmetic texts.

2. Can you find a system in which "2×5" has meaning, but "$2 \times 5 = 10$" is meaningless? Look into modular, or "clock," arithmetic.

3. In what sense may one say that the postulates of a system define its undefined terms?

4. What are some of the "axioms" in the Declaration of Independence?

Chapter 2

SENTENTIAL VARIABLES,

OPERATORS, AND FORMULAS

2-1 INTRODUCTION

In this chapter we shall examine relations among statements, the synthesis of statements from, and their analysis into other statements, and the effects and properties of grammatical operations. For the time being, we can think of a statement as a declarative sentence of the kind commonly met with in mathematics, *independently of any consideration of truth or falsity*. Some examples are:

Base angles of an isosceles triangle are congruent.

Tan $60° = 2$.

If $x \neq 0$, then $z > 0$.

For any $h > 0$ there is a $k > 0$ such that if $0 < |x_1 - x_2| < h$, then $|f(x_1) - f(x_2)| < k$.

Here we seem to be already departing from a program of strict formalism. You may feel that in order to recognize the sentential nature of a substatement, for example, it would be necessary to grasp the *meaning* of the symbols. However, as far as we are concerned in setting forth the rules of the game, we shall not be *using* particular statements; instead, we shall be *discussing* statements in general. We shall therefore use symbols to *represent* statements, and there will be no ambiguity about their presentation as such. It will only be in applications and examples that actual statements will be seen.

In any particular mathematical system that has been presented in a format keyed to our rules, there would be explicit directions for constructing statements, as we said in Chapter 1. The admittance of a formula† such as $x > y$

† Throughout this text, "formula" simply means a string of symbols.

as a statement might be brought about by a definition equating it with an already established statement form, or by taking it as a primitive, undefined form, classified by proclamation as a statement.

2-2 SENTENTIAL VARIABLES AND SENTENTIAL FORMULAS

Our symbolism starts with the agreement to use the capital letters A, B, P, Q, R, S, T, H, and C, sometimes with subscripts, to stand for statements in general. In analogy with usage at the mathematical level (as distinguished from the logical level), we shall call these letters **sentential variables**, when so used. Formulas involving such symbols will be called **sentential formulas**. There are many ways to form statements from other statements, but, for our purposes, we can restrict our attention to five grammatical operations, and two modifying phrases which will be introduced in Chapter 4.

EXERCISES

Which of the following are statements in the sense described in this section?

1. When $x > 2$, then $x^2 > 4$.

2. Two triangles that are congruent are similar.

3. Two triangles that are similar are congruent.

4. The product of two numbers.

5. Find the area of the rectangle.

6. Every triangle is a polygon.

7. $120 = 5!$.

8. $a(b + c)^2$.

9. $x^2 + 2x = 5$.

10. $AB \perp CD$.

11. Is $\sqrt{2}$ a rational number?

12. Never divide by zero!

2-3 NEGATION

The first and simplest operation is that of general negation. Verbally, this may be done by prefixing "It is false that_____," or, more commonly, by internal negation. Thus "*b* is a rational number" becomes "*b* is not a rational number," "$x = 5$" becomes "$x \neq 5$," and so on. Note that "*b* is an irrational number" is not a general negation of the given statement (see Exercise 1). Symbolically, we shall denote the general negation of *P* by $\sim P$. The prefixed symbol is called a tilde.

EXERCISES

1. Why is "*b* is an irrational number" not a general negation of "*b* is a rational number"? (Consider various possible interpretations for *b*.)

2. Discuss the distinction between the opposite of a statement and the general negation of a statement.

3. If every statement must be either true or false, then $\sim[\sim P]$ has the same meaning as *P*, whatever statement *P* is. Consider a system of logic in which statements can have any one of three values, say, "true," "false," and "maybe." Would $\sim[\sim P]$ then necessarily be interchangeable with *P*? Discuss.

2-4 CONJUNCTION AND DISJUNCTION

From a statement *P* and a statement *Q* we can form a new statement *P and Q*. There are other English conjunctions that have the same logical content as "and," although their connotation, or pyschological content, may differ. Outstanding examples are "but" and "however". Whatever the verbalization may be, we symbolize the logical conjunction of *P* and *Q* by $P \wedge Q$.

The word "or" has more than one meaning in English, but the one that is generally used in logic is that of nonexclusive choice. To assert "*x* is rational or it is negative" does not mean that it cannot be both rational *and* negative.

We shall use consistently the interpretation that at least one of the choices must hold, and both may hold. We symbolize the logical disjunction of P and Q by $P \vee Q$.

EXERCISES

1. Find some other English words or phrases having the same logical content as "and."

2. Find some other English words or phrases having the same logical content as "or."

2-5 THE CONDITIONAL

One of the most familiar forms of compound mathematical statements is *If P, then Q*. Equivalent wordings are *If P, Q*; *P only if Q*; *Q if P*; and *Q when P*. Note that in the last two wordings, the substatement P comes after the substatement Q. We shall represent them all by $P \Rightarrow Q$. The arrow is sometimes verbalized as "implies," but there are at least two objections to that reading. In the first place, the blanks in "_____ implies _____" should be filled with substantives rather than substatements, from a purely grammatical point of view. If P is the statement "John is sick," and Q is "he stays home," then "$P \Rightarrow Q$" can be translated "If John is sick, then he stays home." But to translate it as "John is sick implies he stays home" is a clear violation of English grammar. Of course, we may write " 'John is sick' implies 'he stays home.' " Here the blanks have been filled with expressions that happen to be the names of statements, as indicated by the inner quotation marks. However, this brings us to the second objection. In the latter rendering, we are making a statement about statements, which is not the same thing as a statement about John's behavior. This is why many logicians prefer to reserve "implies" for a relation between statements, such as deducibility of the second from the first.

On the other hand, owing to the lack of a single word to verbalize this operator, "implies" is excusable for its convenience, in oral usage.

In a conditional, $P \Rightarrow Q$, the substatement P is called the **antecedent**, and Q is called the **consequent**.

EXERCISES

Determine whether each of the following statements *as a whole* can be represented by a conditional formula. For each one that can be so represented, write out the antecedent and the consequent.

1. When it rains, it pours.

2. If you cut your finger, then you bleed; but if you cut your hair, then you do not bleed.

3. One should buy yachts only if one is rich.

4. (a) For x^2 to be greater than zero, it is necessary that x be different from zero.
   (b) For x^2 to be greater than zero, it is sufficient that x be different from zero.

5. (a) A triangle is isosceles if it is equilateral.
   (b) A triangle is equilateral only if it is isosceles.

6. If x is real and y is real, then xy is real and so is $x + y$.

7. If x is real, then when y is real, so is $x + y$, and when y is imaginary, so is $x + y$.

8. When the bough breaks, the cradle will fall.

9. My heart leaps up when I behold a rainbow in the sky.

10. I do not know when the cradle will fall.

11. If we should fail?

12. When beggars die, there are no comets seen.

The sentences above include several versions of the conditional.

13. What verbalizations of the conditional can you find in Exercises 1 through 12?

14. Do you know of any other ways of expressing the conditional?

2-6 THE BICONDITIONAL

For this construction, we shall change our approach. Instead of presenting it on its own, we are going to define it in terms of constructions that have already been discussed.

Definition

$$P \Leftrightarrow Q \quad \text{for} \quad [P \Rightarrow Q] \wedge [Q \Rightarrow P]$$

The form of this definition, $----$ for $.....$, indicates a definition on the symbolic level. The left side can be taken as an abbreviation for the right side, just as SNAFU is a symbol abbreviating a much longer string of symbols.

The right side can be read "If P then Q, and if Q then P," and, by definition, so can the left side. A more convenient reading is "P if and only if Q." Whenever a statement of one form is indicated, the other form may be freely substituted for it on the strength of the definition. One must distinguish between this kind of substitution and that of substituting Q for P *because* $P \Leftrightarrow Q$ holds. The latter kind of substitution will require a special rule, containing certain important restrictions. (See § 5-6.)

EXERCISE

There are other verbalizations for $P \Leftrightarrow Q$. Which ones do you know? (The previous set of exercises may be of help here.)

2-7 BRACKETS AND SCOPE CONVENTIONS. SENTENTIAL OPERATORS

We shall refer to the five symbols $\sim$, $\wedge$, $\vee$, $\Rightarrow$, and $\Leftrightarrow$ as **sentential operators**. The first is a **monary** (or **unary**) **operator**, affecting a single statement, and each of the others is a **binary operator**, involving two statements (not necessarily different) for its use.

In the preceding sections we have used another symbol, bracket pairs, to indicate grouping. Explanations of how they are used should be superfluous to anyone familiar with elementary algebra. We need to reserve parentheses and braces for other purposes, so we shall have to risk confusion by using brackets within brackets. To reduce the number of brackets so used, we shall adopt certain conventions of scope of symbol analogous to the familiar practices of algebraic notation, such as the agreement that $a + bc$ means $a + (bc)$ and not $(a + b)c$, or that ab^2 means $a(b^2)$ and not $(ab)^2$.

The negation symbol will have minimum scope. Thus $\sim P \wedge Q$ will mean $[\sim P] \wedge Q$; $\sim P \Rightarrow Q$ will mean $[\sim P] \Rightarrow Q$; and so on. If it is desired to extend the negation over a compound statement, brackets will have to be used.

Among the binary operators, conjunction and disjunction have the smallest scope. $P \vee Q \Rightarrow R$ will mean $[P \vee Q] \Rightarrow R$, not $P \vee [Q \Rightarrow R]$. A formula like $P \vee Q \wedge R$ is not permitted; it is ambiguous without brackets.†

The conditional comes next, with the biconditional having the greatest scope of all. $P \Rightarrow Q \vee R \Leftrightarrow \sim P \wedge Q$ will mean $[P \Rightarrow [Q \vee R]] \Leftrightarrow [[\sim P] \wedge Q]$. Of course, for the sake of additional clarity, we may elect not to use these conventions.

Another scope convention deals with strings like

$$Q \wedge R \wedge S \wedge T, \quad Q \vee R \vee S \vee T, \quad \text{or} \quad Q \Rightarrow R \Rightarrow S \Rightarrow T$$

Since all the operators except the tilde are binary (that is, they operate only on *pairs* of statements), the foregoing strings are meaningless. We shall adopt the convention that, with a *string involving only one kind of binary operator*, association is to the right in the absence of brackets. The strings above then mean, respectively,

$$Q \wedge [R \wedge [S \wedge T]]$$

$$Q \vee [R \vee [S \vee T]]$$

and $\qquad Q \Rightarrow [R \Rightarrow [S \Rightarrow T]]$

Our convention is contrary to the usual practice in algebra, and also to that of many texts in logic, which use a leftward convention. In subtraction, for example, the usual convention is to take $9 - 4 - 2$ as equal to $(9 - 4) - 2$, rather than $9 - (4 - 2)$. We are adopting the rightward convention with respect to sentential formulas because it is the one that is most useful with the conditional operator. The others obey an associative law, just as addition

† Custom varies in this respect; $\vee$ is sometimes granted greater scope than $\wedge$, but we shall not do so.

and multiplication of numbers do, so it does not matter which convention we use with them. For the sake of formal definiteness, we make the same convention apply to all binary operators. With regard to a repeated tilde, $\sim\sim\sim P$ will mean $\sim[\sim[\sim P]]$.

EXERCISES

Use the scope conventions to eliminate as many brackets as you can from the given formulas.

1. $[\sim P] \vee [Q \Rightarrow P]$

2. $[P \Leftrightarrow Q] \Rightarrow [R \Rightarrow S]$

3. $\sim[P \wedge Q] \Rightarrow [P \vee [Q \vee R]]$

4. $P \wedge [Q \wedge [\sim[R \wedge S]]]$

5. $[P \Rightarrow [P \wedge Q]] \Rightarrow Q$

6. $\sim[[P \vee Q] \vee R] \Rightarrow [S \Leftrightarrow T]$

7. $[P \Leftrightarrow Q] \Leftrightarrow [R \Rightarrow S]$

8. $[P \vee [Q \vee [R \vee S]]] \Leftrightarrow [P \Rightarrow [Q \wedge [R \wedge S]]]$

Supply each of the formulas given below with brackets so that no scope conventions are needed to interpret them.

9. $P \wedge \sim Q \Rightarrow P \wedge R \wedge S$

10. $P \Leftrightarrow \sim R \Rightarrow R \Leftrightarrow \sim P$

11. $Q \Rightarrow P \vee R \Rightarrow \sim P \Rightarrow \sim R$

12. $P \wedge R \wedge S \Rightarrow \sim P \wedge Q$

13. $P \Rightarrow R \vee S \Leftrightarrow \sim P \vee R \vee S$

14. $[P \wedge Q] \Leftrightarrow \sim[\sim P \vee \sim Q]$

15. $\sim P \Rightarrow Q \Leftrightarrow \sim Q \Rightarrow P$

16. $Q \vee P \Rightarrow Q \vee R \Rightarrow P \wedge R$

In the next seven exercises, you are to construct a dictionary of sentential variables† for each statement, breaking it down as far as possible with respect to substatements. Then write the corresponding sentential formula, using the scope conventions where appropriate. If a substatement is in negated form, use the positive form in setting up your dictionary, as has been done with the substatement S in the example given below.

Example

> *Statement:* If $x > 4$ and $y^2 > x$, then $y > 2$ or y is not positive.

> *Dictionary:* P: $x > 4$
> Q: $y^2 > x$
> R: $y > 2$
> S: y is positive

> *Formula:* $P \wedge Q \Rightarrow R \vee {\sim} S$

17. If ABC is a triangle and $\overline{AD}$ bisects angle A, then $BD/CD = AB/AC$ and $(AD)^2 = (AC)(AB) - (AD)(CD)$.

18. If $\angle A \cong \angle B$, then $\overline{AC} \cong \overline{BC}$ and conversely.

19. $|\sin^2 x_1 - \sin^2 x_2| < k$ when $|x_1 - x_2| < h$, if $k > 0$ and $h < k/2$.

‡20. f is continuous at x_0 if and only if $f(x_0)$ is defined and $\lim_{x \to x_0} f(x) = f(x_0)$.

‡21. If $\lim f = a$ and $\lim g = b$, then $\lim fg = ab$, and, provided that $b \neq 0$, $\lim f/g = a/b$.

22. If ABC is a triangle and D is the midpoint of $\overline{AB}$, then $\angle ACB$ is a right angle if $\overline{CD} \cong \overline{AD}$.

23. $x < 0$ only if $x^2 > 0$, and $x > 0$ only if $x^2 > 0$; hence from the fact that $x > 0$ or $x < 0$ when $x \neq 0$, we get $x = 0$ or $x^2 > 0$.

---

† Strictly speaking, we should call them sentential *constants* in the context of a dictionary, because in each problem your dictionary assigns a unique statement as the "value" of the capital letter involved.

‡ You should be able to do these even if you do not quite understand the meaning of the statements involved.

Sometimes it is useful to break up a sentence that has a compound subject or predicate, rephrasing it by using two or more substatements with simple subjects and predicates. For example,

> x and y are each positive or zero

can be rephrased as

> x is positive or x is zero, and y is positive or y is zero

Exercises 24 and 25 should be handled that way. For Exercises 24, 25, and 26, you are to assume that the "universe of discourse" is the system of real numbers. In that case, "x is an irrational number" may be taken to be a general negation of "x is a rational number."

24. Write a formula for the following statement, using the given dictionary.

> *Statement:* $\sqrt{5}$ and $4 - \sqrt{5}$ are both irrational numbers, but $\sqrt{5} + (4 - \sqrt{5}) = 4$, which is a rational number.

> *Dictionary:* P: $\sqrt{5}$ is a rational number
> $\quad\quad\quad\quad\, Q$: $4 - \sqrt{5}$ is a rational number
> $\quad\quad\quad\quad\, R$: $\sqrt{5} + (4 - \sqrt{5}) = 4$
> $\quad\quad\quad\quad\, S$: 4 is a rational number

25. Write a dictionary and a formula for the following statement.

> *Statement:* The sum of the numbers x and y is rational only if both are rational or both are irrational.

26. Rephrase the following statement, introducing an x and a y. Then write a dictionary and a formula for the statement.

> *Statement:* The product of two numbers is irrational only if one of them is irrational and the other rational and not zero.

27. (a) How many possible interpretations could be given to $P * Q * R$, just by inserting brackets? Assume that $*$ is a nonassociative binary operator.
(b) Repeat part (a) for $P * Q * R * S$.

Chapter 3

TRUTH TABLES.

THE SENTENTIAL CALCULUS

3-1 BASIC TRUTH TABLES

In Chapter 2 we introduced the sentential operators from a standpoint of meanings. In this chapter we shall consider them from an operational standpoint. In that sense, the basic truth tables given below define each operator for our purposes, because the tables ultimately determine what we can and what we cannot permit in the way of formal manipulation with the operators.

In ordinary discourse, if a sentence is compounded of subordinate clauses by means of the five grammatical operations discussed in Chapter 2, then its truth or falsity will depend entirely on the truth or falsity of the substatements, and the way that they have been put together. If we can determine, for each substatement, whether it is true or false, we can then determine the truth or falsity of the compound statement by what amounts to a calculation. For example, if P is a meaningful statement, a committee of experts might have certain difficulties in reaching an agreement as to whether it is true or false,† but everyone would agree that if P is true, then $\sim P$ is false, and if P is false, then $\sim P$ is true. We shall accept this as a definition of the operator $\sim$, and exhibit it in the form of a **truth table**.

Table 1a

P	$\sim P$
T	F
F	T

† In fact, one can question whether it makes sense to consider a statement such as $x > 0$ as either true or false, without having more information about x.

A statement of the form $P \land Q$ is considered to be true if and only if P and Q are each true statements. Accordingly, the truth table for the operator $\land$ is shown in Table 1b.

Table 1b

P	Q	$P \land Q$
T	T	T
T	F	F
F	T	F
F	F	F

Coming now to the disjunction, $P \lor Q$, everyone readily agrees that if just one substatement is true, the disjunction is true; and that if both substatements are false, the disjunction is false. But some students boggle at accepting the truth of the remaining case, as illustrated by the sentence "California is on the West Coast, or Oregon is." It is a fact that "or" is at times used in a context that connotes "but not both," and at other times in a context that connotes "or both." We must at all times avoid ambiguity in our basic operators, so we must choose between the two meanings in setting up our truth table. Only because it turns out to be more convenient, logicians have chosen the inclusive interpretation over the exclusive one.

Table 1c

P	Q	$P \lor Q$
T	T	T
T	F	T
F	T	T
F	F	F

The definition of the conditional operator causes even more distress to some people. According to the rule that we shall adopt, a conditional will be said to be false if and only if it has a true antecedent and a false consequent. This means that when Q is true, then $P \Rightarrow Q$ is true no matter whether P is true or false. Even more paradoxically, if P is false, then $P \Rightarrow Q$ is true, no matter whether Q is true or false! With this usage, we are adopting what is called the "material conditional" (or "material implication"). It is not the only reasonable meaning for "If _____ , then _____" constructions. There are other usages with important claims on the logician's attention,† but this is the one found in mathematical discourse. Actually, the material conditional is not unknown to common speech. The man who says "If he's a logician, then I'm a two-headed calf" is making an assertion that he wishes to be accepted as a true statement. He hopes that you will notice the falsity of the consequent, that from this you will infer the falsity of the antecedent, and so come to understand that the person under discussion is no logician. Consider also the familiar expression of an unfortunate situation: "You're hanged if you do, and you're hanged if you don't." This has the form

$$[P \Rightarrow Q] \wedge [\sim P \Rightarrow Q]$$

For the statement to be true, each of the conjoined conditionals must be true (see Table 1b). However, P and $\sim P$ cannot both be true, so one of the presumably true conditionals has a false antecedent.

We hope that the foregoing discussion has made the definition of the conditional in Table 1d more palatable.

Table 1d

P	Q	$P \Rightarrow Q$
T	T	T
T	F	F
F	T	T
F	F	T

† See, for example, I. M. Copi, *Introduction to Logic* (New York: Macmillan, 1953), pp. 229–252.

Along with the preceding tables, the definition of the biconditional now determines the entries in a table for that operator. Note that by Table 1b, the biconditional will have the value T if and only if $P \Rightarrow Q$ and $Q \Rightarrow P$ both have the value T. By Table 1d, this means that P and Q will have to be both true, or both false.

Table 1e

P	Q	$P \Leftrightarrow Q$
T	T	T
T	F	F
F	T	F
F	F	T

For convenience of comparison and reference, we have combined Tables 1a through 1e in Table 1.

Table 1

P	Q	$\sim P$	$P \wedge Q$	$P \vee Q$	$P \Rightarrow Q$	$P \Leftrightarrow Q$
T	T	F	T	T	T	T
T	F	F	F	T	F	F
F	T	T	F	T	T	F
F	F	T	F	F	T	T

Summary

1. The truth value of a statement is opposite to that of its negation.

2. A conjunction is true when and only when both of its substatements are true.

3. A disjunction is false when and only when both of its substatements are false.

4. A conditional is false when and only when its antecedent is true and its consequent is false.

5. A biconditional is true when and only when the substatements are both true or both false.

EXERCISES

1. For each of the following sentences, state whether "or" has been used in the inclusive or exclusive sense.

   (a) He does not go out if it is raining or it is cold.
   (b) Let us do or die.
   (c) Would Madam like some coffee, or does she prefer tea?
   (d) To be or not to be, that is the question.
   (e) Fish or cut bait.

2. The formula $P \Leftrightarrow Q$ is sometimes read "P is a necessary and sufficient condition for Q." Clearly, this indicates that "P is a sufficient condition for Q" must be one of $P \Rightarrow Q$ or $Q \Rightarrow P$, while "P is a necessary condition for Q" must be the other. Make a choice, and give an argument defending it.

3. (a) Construct a truth table for $P \underline{\vee} Q$, where $\underline{\vee}$ represents the exclusive interpretation of "or."
   (b) Let P and Q represent the following statements:

   > P: John can vote in this state.
   > Q: John is under 21 years old.

   Note that all four combinations of truth values for P and Q are possible, since John may or may not meet other voting qualifications of "this state," and "this state" may or may not have a minimum voting age of 21. With this in mind, construct a truth table for the statement:

   > John can vote in this state unless John is under 21 years old.

3-2 TRUTH TABLES FOR COMPOUND SENTENCES

Now, with Table 1 as a guide, we can construct a table for any compound statement to show just how its truth value depends on the truth values of its substatements. Let us take the formula

$$[P \Rightarrow Q] \wedge [P \Rightarrow \sim R] \Leftrightarrow [P \Rightarrow Q \vee R]$$

The final result will be shown as Table 2, but we must proceed step by step in constructing it. Our table will have to have 2^3 lines, because each of the three independent sentential variables may be either true or false. (Calling the variables "independent" means just that we are assuming that all eight combinations are possible.) Please observe the pattern. Under the heading R, T and F alternate; under Q, T and F alternate in pairs; under P they alternate by fours. This ensures that no two of the triplets are identical, and all possible triplets have been listed.

P	Q	R	
T	T	T	
T	T	F	
T	F	T	
T	F	F	
F	T	T	
F	T	F	
F	F	T	
F	F	F	

We now consider each of the subformulas, working up from the simplest to the more complex ones. We observe an occurrence of $\sim R$, and start with that. All we have to do is observe the R column and write down the opposite truth values.

P	Q	R	$\sim R$
T	T	T	F
T	T	F	T
T	F	T	F
T	F	F	T
F	T	T	F
F	T	F	T
F	F	T	F
F	F	F	T

Another relatively simple subformula is $Q \vee R$. We obtain its values by examining the Q and R columns, and writing entries under $Q \vee R$ in accordance with Table 1. One easy way to do this is to spot the FF combinations for Q and R, writing F for these, and filling in the other spaces with T.

P	Q	R	$\sim R$	$Q \vee R$
T	T	T	F	T
T	T	F	T	T
T	F	T	F	T
T	F	F	T	F
F	T	T	F	T
F	T	F	T	T
F	F	T	F	T
F	F	F	T	F

We are now ready to complete columns for each of the conditional sub-formulas. This time we look for the TF combinations, filling in the rest afterward.

P	Q	R	$\sim R$	$Q \vee R$	$P \Rightarrow Q$	$P \Rightarrow \sim R$	$P \Rightarrow Q \vee R$	
T	T	T	F	T	T	F	T	
T	T	F	T	T	T	T	T	
T	F	T	F	T	F	F	T	
T	F	F	T	F	F	T	F	
F	T	T	F	T	T	T	T	
F	T	F	T	T	T	T	T	
F	F	T	F	T	T	T	T	
F	F	F	T	F	T	T	T	

We next conjoin $P \Rightarrow Q$ and $P \Rightarrow \sim R$, to get the left side of the biconditional. This time we spot the TT combinations, entering T for each one, filling in the rest with F. Finally we work on the biconditional. To save space, we have abbreviated the column headings in a self-explanatory manner.

From Table 2 we see that the given formula is false when and only when P and R are both true.

EXERCISES

Construct a truth table for each of the formulas below. Please use the recommended pattern for your entries under the sentential variables.

1. $P \wedge Q \Rightarrow P$

2. $\sim[P \Rightarrow Q] \Leftrightarrow P \wedge \sim Q$

Table 2

			A	B	C	D	E	F	G
P	Q	R	$\sim R$	$Q \vee R$	$P \Rightarrow Q$	$P \Rightarrow \sim R$	$P \Rightarrow B$	$C \wedge D$	$F \Leftrightarrow E$
T	T	T	F	T	T	F	T	F	F
T	T	F	T	T	T	T	T	T	T
T	F	T	F	T	F	F	T	F	F
T	F	F	T	F	F	T	F	F	T
F	T	T	F	T	T	T	T	T	T
F	T	F	T	T	T	T	T	T	T
F	F	T	F	T	T	T	T	T	T
F	F	F	T	F	T	T	T	T	T

3. $P \Rightarrow P \wedge Q$

4. $P \wedge [Q \Rightarrow P]$

5. $P \vee Q \Rightarrow P$

6. $P \vee [Q \Rightarrow P]$

7. $[P \vee Q] \vee R \Leftrightarrow P \vee [Q \vee R]$

8. $[P \vee Q \Leftrightarrow Q \wedge R] \Rightarrow \sim Q$

3-3 TAUTOLOGIES

In some of the exercises of the preceding section, for example in Exercise 7, all the last-column entries turned out to be T. In other words any state-ment of the form given in that exercise would be true, irrespective of whether its substatements were true or false. Statements having that property play a special role, and we shall call them **truth-table tautologies.** More precisely,

> a sentential formula that has the value T for all possible combinations of truth values for its sentential variables is a **tautological formula**; a statement that can be represented by a tautological formula is a **truth-table tautology.**

Although the word "tautology" stands for a much wider class of statements, we shall use it from here on as short for "truth-table tautology." It can also be used as an abstract noun, meaning "the property of being tautological, as in "Test that statement for tautology."†

In asking whether or not a statement is a tautology, we again seem to be involved in questions of meaning, for surely meaning is inseparable from matters of truth or falsity. However, the fact is that in applying our rules, we shall only be interested in whether a given statement is a truth-table tautology or not. One can compare the situation with a study of trigonometry that is undertaken with the promise that there will be no numerical computations. A legitimate part of such study would be the proving of the so-called "identities," but to assert that "$\sin 2\alpha = 2 \sin \alpha \cos \alpha$" is an identity is equivalent to asserting that "$\sin 2\alpha - 2 \sin \alpha \cos \alpha$" defines a function that has a constant numerical value of zero. Does the proof of an identity thereby involve numerical computation? In exact analogy, $P \Rightarrow P \vee Q$ defines a sentential function with a constant value T. Once we accept the rules of Table 1, no problem of meaning will be involved in determining whether a particular statement is a tautology, once we have found a sentential formula appropriate to the statement.

EXERCISES

1. Show that the statement in Exercise 17 of § 2-7 is not tautological.

2. Show that the statement in Exercise 18 of § 2-7 is not tautological.

3. Each of the statements tested in Exercises 1 and 2 are provable in plane geometry. Why are they not tautological?

The last column for the truth table for Exercise 5 of the preceding section turned out to be identical with the last column of the truth table for $Q \Rightarrow P$.

---

† Some of our best-loved cliches are elementary tautologies; "Cheap is cheap," for example, or "When y'gotta go, y'gotta go."

Thus

$$[P \vee Q \Rightarrow P] \Leftrightarrow [Q \Rightarrow P]$$

is tautological, and, in that sense, $Q \Rightarrow P$ may be said to be "logically equivalent" to $P \vee Q \Rightarrow P$. (A more general definition of logical equivalence is given in a later chapter.) Sometimes we can even find a formula logically equivalent to, but using fewer distinct sentential variables than, a given one. For example, the formula $P \wedge [Q \Rightarrow P]$ is logically equivalent to P alone, showing that the truth or falsity of Q has no effect on the truth or falsity of $P \wedge [Q \Rightarrow P]$. In Exercises 4 through 7, state the shortest formula that you can find which is logically equivalent to the given one.

4. $P \Rightarrow P \wedge Q$

5. $P \vee [Q \Rightarrow P]$

6. $P \wedge Q \Rightarrow R \Leftrightarrow P \vee [Q \wedge R]$

7. $[P \vee Q \Leftrightarrow Q \wedge R] \Rightarrow \sim Q$

3-4 A SHORT TEST FOR TAUTOLOGY

If one is only interested in checking a given formula for tautology, there are methods that are usually (but not always) shorter than setting up a complete table. If we wish to test, say, the formula

$$P \wedge Q \Rightarrow P \vee R$$

we might proceed as follows:

> For a conditional to be false, the antecedent has to be true and the consequent false. For the given antecedent, $P \wedge Q$, to be true, both P and Q must be true. For the given consequent, $P \vee Q$, to be false, both P and R must be false. Since P cannot be true in one occurrence and false in another, it is impossible for the given formula to be false, and it is therefore tautological.

We can schematize an argument such as this by assigning the truth value F to the formula, then working down through the subformulas to the sentential variable. If the formula is in fact tautological, then we shall be inescapably led to a contradiction. To assign a value to a compound formula, we write the value underneath the operator. In a short test of the formula given above, we start by copying down the formula and writing F, as shown below.

Example 1

Test the following formula for tautology.

$$P \wedge Q \Rightarrow P \vee Q$$
$$\text{F}$$

We now must assign T to the antecedent, and F to the consequent. Note the location of these letters.

$$P \wedge Q \Rightarrow P \vee R$$
$$\text{F}$$
$$\text{T} \qquad \text{F}$$

We now write the values for the sentential variables, as determined by the value assignments up to this point.

$$P \wedge Q \Rightarrow P \vee R$$
$$\text{F}$$
$$\text{T} \qquad \text{F}$$
$$\text{T} \quad \text{T} \quad \text{F} \quad \text{F}$$

The unavoidable contradiction has been indicated above.

Sometimes more than one case must be considered. In the next example, the main sentential operator is a biconditional, which can be false in two ways (see Table 1e). In case 1 we consider the possibility of a true left side and a false right side. To the right of each step we have indicated a reason for it.

Example 2

Test the following formula for tautology.

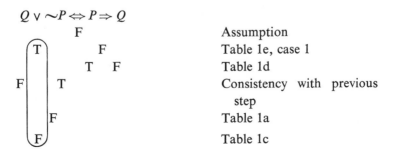

$Q \vee {\sim}P \Leftrightarrow P \Rightarrow Q$	
F	Assumption
T F	Table 1e, case 1
T F	Table 1d
F T	Consistency with previous step
F	Table 1a
F	Table 1c

In case 2 we consider the possibility of a true right side of the biconditional, and a false left side.

$$Q \vee \sim P \Leftrightarrow P \Rightarrow Q$$

F	Assumption
F T	Table 1e, case 2
F F	
T	
T F	
F	

We have left the last four reasons as an exercise. Since *both* cases led to a contradiction, the given formula is tautological.

In a complicated formula, cases within cases may develop. In that event, the full truth-table approach may be preferred.

If the procedure leads to a consistent assignment of values to the variables, with no contradiction, then the formula being tested is not tautological.

Example 3

Test the following formula for tautology.

$$P \wedge Q \Leftrightarrow P \wedge [Q \vee R]$$

F	
T F	Table 1e, case 1
T T	
T T	
T	
T	

Notice that we came to a contradiction without assigning any value to *R*. But we are not finished—the contradiction has not been shown to be inevitable, for we must explore case 2.

$$P \wedge Q \Leftrightarrow P \wedge [Q \vee R]$$

F
F   T
     T   T
T
  F
     F
      T

The given formula is *not* tautological, because it can be false if P and R are true, and Q is false.

We shall refer to this process as a **short method of testing for tautology.** With a little practice, it becomes fairly rapid.

EXERCISES

1. Supply the reasoning for each step of the second part of Example 2.

2. Supply the reasoning for each step of Example 3.

Test each of the following formulas for tautology by a short method. If the formula is not tautological, give one set of truth values of the sentential variables involved for which the formula is false.

3. $\sim P \Rightarrow P \Rightarrow Q$

4. $[P \Rightarrow Q] \Rightarrow [\sim P \Rightarrow \sim Q]$

5. $\sim[P \vee Q] \Leftrightarrow \sim P \wedge \sim Q$

6. $P \vee Q \Rightarrow R$

7. $[P \Leftrightarrow Q \wedge R] \Rightarrow [\sim R \Rightarrow \sim P]$

8. $[P \Rightarrow Q] \wedge [Q \Rightarrow R] \Rightarrow [P \Rightarrow R]$

9. $[P \Rightarrow Q \wedge \sim R] \vee [P \wedge \sim R]$

10. $P \wedge Q \Rightarrow R \Leftrightarrow P \vee [Q \wedge R]$

3-5 CHOICE OF FORMULAS

In writing a formula for a statement to be tested, there will sometimes be some latitude as to what substatements should be represented by a single variable. Of course, if a certain substatement or its negation appears more than once, and P has been used for one occurrence of this statement, then P should be used for every occurrence, and $\sim P$ for every occurrence of its negation. Consider the statement

> If there is a fight whenever Brown and Smith are both at a party, then a party that was peaceful was not attended by both Brown and Smith.

If we use the dictionary

> P: Brown attends the party
> Q: Smith attends the party
> R: The party is peaceful

then the content of the statement may be reasonably approximated by the formula

$$[P \wedge Q \Rightarrow \sim R] \Rightarrow [R \Rightarrow \sim [P \wedge Q]]$$

Testing this formula by a short method, we find that the statement is a tautology.

If we had noticed that the separate attendance of Brown and Smith was never considered in the original statement, we could have let S represent "Brown and Smith are at the party." The corresponding formula would then have been

$$[S \Rightarrow \sim R] \Rightarrow [R \Rightarrow \sim S]$$

which still tests out as a tautology.

Such abridgement has its dangers. Consider the statement

> If the moon is new, then it is raining or it is not raining.

If we use the dictionary:

> P: The moon is new
> Q: It is raining or it is not raining

then the statement appears to have the form $P \Rightarrow Q$, which is not tautological. But if we use

> P: The moon is new
> R: It is raining

then the statement has the form $P \Rightarrow R \vee \sim R$, which is tautological. The catch here is that the substatements of $R \vee \sim R$ are not independent; they cannot take on all possible combinations of truth values. In fact, in the formula $P \Rightarrow Q$ above, the Q is such that it always has the value T. In that case, $P \Rightarrow Q$ must have the value T whatever P may be.

EXERCISES

For Exercises 1, 2, and 3, use the following dictionary and test the given statement for tautology.

> P: x is rational R: xy is rational
> Q: y is rational S: $xy = 0$

Assume the real numbers to be the universe of discourse, so that "x is irrational" is the general negation of "x is rational."

1. If xy is rational when x and y are rational, then when y is irrational, xy is irrational.

2. If xy is rational when x and y are rational, then when y is irrational and xy is irrational, x is irrational.

3. xy is rational and nonzero only if x and y are both rational or both irrational; but it is false that if x and y are both irrational, then xy is irrational.

4. Write your own dictionary and test for tautology: x is not an even perfect number if and only if x is not an even number and x is not a perfect number.

5. Write your own dictionary and test for tautology: If triangle ABC must be scalene or isosceles, then, when it is not scalene, it must be isosceles.

6. Write your own dictionary and test for tautology: The fact that triangle ABC is similar and equiareal with triangle EFG if and only if triangle ABC

is congruent to triangle *EFG* implies that if triangle *ABC* is not congruent to triangle *EFG*, then it is not similar to triangle *EFG*.

7. An example was given in this section showing that a statement which was actually a tautology failed to show that property under too coarse an analysis. Is it possible that a statement which is actually not a tautology would appear to be one under too coarse an analysis? Discuss.

3-6 USEFUL TAUTOLOGICAL FORMULAS

Out of the infinitude of possible tautological formulas, the list below includes only some that are most generally useful. The list need not be memorized, because any question as to the tautological nature of formulas as simple as these may be easily settled. However, a general familiarity with the contents of the list will be helpful in the exercises and in future chapters.

The first five formulas are useful for negating complex statements (see § 9-2).

$$(1) \quad \sim\sim P \Leftrightarrow P$$

$$(2) \quad \sim[P \wedge Q] \Leftrightarrow \sim P \vee \sim Q$$

$$(3) \quad \sim[P \vee Q] \Leftrightarrow \sim P \wedge \sim Q$$

$$(4) \quad \sim[P \Rightarrow Q] \Leftrightarrow P \wedge \sim Q$$

$$(5) \quad (a) \quad \sim[P \Leftrightarrow Q] \Leftrightarrow [\sim P \Leftrightarrow Q]$$

$$(b) \quad \sim[P \Leftrightarrow Q] \Leftrightarrow [P \Leftrightarrow \sim Q]$$

The next three formulas are commutative laws.

$$(6) \quad P \wedge Q \Leftrightarrow Q \wedge P$$

$$(7) \quad P \vee Q \Leftrightarrow Q \vee P$$

$$(8) \quad [P \Leftrightarrow Q] \Leftrightarrow [Q \Leftrightarrow P]$$

The next three formulas are laws of associativity.

$$(9) \quad [P \wedge Q] \wedge R \Leftrightarrow P \wedge [Q \wedge R]$$

$$(10) \quad [P \vee Q] \vee R \Leftrightarrow P \vee [Q \vee R]$$

$$(11) \quad [[P \Leftrightarrow Q] \Leftrightarrow R] \Leftrightarrow [P \Leftrightarrow [Q \Leftrightarrow R]]$$

Notice that the conditional is neither commutative nor associative. The next seven formulas are distributive laws, involving two distinct operators and three distinct sentential variables. Formulas (12) and (13) show that conjunction and disjunction are each distributive over the other.

(12) $P \wedge [Q \vee R] \Leftrightarrow [P \wedge Q] \vee [P \wedge R]$

(13) $P \vee [Q \wedge R] \Leftrightarrow [P \vee Q] \wedge [P \vee R]$

In considering distributivity of the conditional over the other binary operators, we must consider left and right distributivity separately, since the conditional is not commutative; for example, $P \Rightarrow [Q \wedge R]$ must be considered separately from $[Q \wedge R] \Rightarrow P$. It turns out that the conditional is left distributive over conjunction and disjunction [formulas (14) and (15)] but not right distributive [formulas (28) and (29), and Exercises 3 and 4].

(14) $P \Rightarrow [Q \wedge R] \Leftrightarrow [P \Rightarrow Q] \wedge [P \Rightarrow R]$

(15) $P \Rightarrow [Q \vee R] \Leftrightarrow [P \Rightarrow Q] \vee [P \Rightarrow R]$

Disjunction is distributive over the conditional, but conjunction is not.

(16) $[P \Rightarrow Q] \vee R \Leftrightarrow [P \vee R] \Rightarrow [Q \vee R]$

The biconditional distributes over conjunction, and disjunction distributes over the biconditional.

(17) $[P \Leftrightarrow [Q \wedge R]] \Leftrightarrow [P \Leftrightarrow Q] \wedge [P \Leftrightarrow R]$

(18) $[P \vee [Q \Leftrightarrow R]] \Leftrightarrow [[P \vee Q] \Leftrightarrow [P \vee R]]$

Many of the remaining formulas have traditional names (also many of the preceding ones) of which we give three as samples.†

(19) $P \Leftrightarrow P$ Reflexivity of the Biconditional

(20) $P \vee \sim P$ Excluded Middle

† For a good listing of names, see H. LeBlanc, *An Introduction to Logic* (New York: Wiley, 1955) pp. 16ff.

(21) $\sim[P \wedge \sim P]$ Contradiction

(22) $[P \wedge P] \Leftrightarrow P$

(23) $[P \vee P] \Leftrightarrow P$

(24) $[P \Rightarrow Q] \Leftrightarrow [\sim Q \Rightarrow \sim P]$

(25) $[P \Leftrightarrow Q] \Leftrightarrow [\sim P \Leftrightarrow \sim Q]$

(26) $[P \Rightarrow Q \wedge \sim Q] \Leftrightarrow \sim P$

(27) $[P \wedge Q \Rightarrow R] \Leftrightarrow [P \Rightarrow [Q \Rightarrow R]]$

(28) $[P \wedge Q \Rightarrow R] \Leftrightarrow [P \Rightarrow R] \vee [Q \Rightarrow R]$

(29) $[P \vee Q \Rightarrow R] \Leftrightarrow [P \Rightarrow R] \wedge [Q \Rightarrow R]$

(30) $[P \wedge Q] \vee P \Leftrightarrow P$

(31) $[P \vee Q] \wedge P \Leftrightarrow P$

(32) $[P \Rightarrow Q] \Leftrightarrow [\sim P \vee R]$

Except for formulas (20) and (21), all the preceding formulas had the biconditional as the dominating operator. From each of these we can get two tautological formulas in the form of conditionals. Thus formula (27) gives us

$$[P \Rightarrow [Q \Rightarrow R]] \Rightarrow [P \wedge Q \Rightarrow R]$$

and $[P \wedge Q \Rightarrow R] \Rightarrow [P \Rightarrow [Q \Rightarrow R]]$

each of which is tautological. Formula (19) yields two identical ones. The remaining formulas have the conditional as the dominating operator.

(33) $P \wedge [P \Rightarrow Q] \Rightarrow Q$

(34) $P \Rightarrow P \vee Q$

(35) (a) $P \wedge Q \Rightarrow P$
       (b) $P \wedge Q \Rightarrow Q$

(36) $P \Rightarrow [Q \Rightarrow P \wedge Q]$

(37) $Q \Rightarrow [P \Rightarrow Q]$

(38) $\sim P \Rightarrow [P \Rightarrow Q]$

(39) $P \wedge [Q \Rightarrow R] \Rightarrow [Q \Rightarrow P \wedge R]$

(40) $[P \Rightarrow Q] \wedge [Q \Rightarrow R] \Rightarrow [P \Rightarrow R]$

(41) $[P \Rightarrow R] \wedge [Q \Rightarrow R] \Rightarrow [P \wedge Q \Rightarrow R]$

(42) $[P \vee Q \Rightarrow R] \Rightarrow [P \Rightarrow R] \vee [Q \Rightarrow R]$

EXERCISES

1. Give an informal argument proving the truth of the following statement. If S and T are sentential formulas and $S \Leftrightarrow T$ is tautological, then $S \Rightarrow T$ and $T \Rightarrow S$ are each tautological.

2. Investigate the possibility of distributive laws involving the biconditional with each of the other binary operators.

3. Find statements for P, Q, and R such that the converse of formula (41) is false.

4. Find statements for P, Q, and R such that the converse of formula (42) is false.

3-7 REDUCING THE NUMBER OF BASIC OPERATORS

In Chapter 2 we took four operators as basic, and defined a fifth operator in terms of two of them. It is worth noting that all five operators could have been defined in terms of negation and conjunction, in terms of negation and disjunction, or in terms of negation and the conditional. In any application of a logic that uses our interpretation of "or," asserting the truth of $P \vee Q$ is equivalent to asserting that P and Q are not both false, or to asserting that it is false that P is false and Q is false. This last version could be represented by $\sim[\sim P \wedge \sim Q]$. Thus we may write

$$P \vee Q \quad \text{for} \quad \sim[\sim P \wedge \sim Q]$$

as a definition of disjunction, because the truth tables for the two formulas have identical last columns.

To find a definition of the conditional in terms of negation and conjunction, we note that the truth table for $P \Rightarrow Q$ shows three T's and one F, while the table for conjunction has the reverse situation. This suggests that we somehow make the TT—T line of Table 1a correspond to the TF—F line of Table 1d. This can be done by reversing values on Q, and then on the whole formula. Thus we could take

$$P \Rightarrow Q \quad \text{for} \quad \sim[P \wedge \sim Q]$$

as the definition of the conditional. For more games like this, see the exercises.

EXERCISES

1. Express $P \Leftrightarrow Q$ in terms of P, Q, $\sim$, and $\wedge$.

2. Express $P \wedge Q$, $P \Rightarrow Q$, and $P \Leftrightarrow Q$ in terms of P, Q, $\sim$, and $\vee$.

3. Express $P \wedge Q$, $P \vee Q$, and $P \Leftrightarrow Q$ in terms of P, Q, $\sim$, and $\Rightarrow$.

It is impossible to define all five operators in terms of any one of them. However, there is an operator, $|$, sometimes called the "Sheffer stroke symbol," which can be used to define them all. Its truth table is given here.

P	Q	$P \mid Q$
T	T	F
T	F	T
F	T	T
F	F	T

With a single basic operator, we can dispense with brackets. To indicate greater scope, we merely use multiple strokes. Instead of writing

$$[[P \mid Q] \mid R] \mid [P \mid R]$$

we can write

$$P \mid Q \parallel R \parallel\mid P \mid R$$

Each multiple stroke includes in its scope to right and left everything between it and a stroke of greater multiplicity. This scope will not include any stroke of equal multiplicity when properly done.

4. (a) Construct a truth table for $P \mid P$ and for $P \mid Q \parallel P \mid Q$.
  (b) Compare your results in (a) with Table 1. What do you find?

5. Using your results in Exercises 1 and 4, define all of the original operators in terms of the stroke operator.

6. Define the stroke operator in terms of
  (a) $\sim$ and $\wedge$.
  (b) $\sim$ and $\vee$.
  (c) $\sim$ and $\Rightarrow$.

7. As in Exercises 4, 5, and 6, investigate the operator $*$, with the truth table given here.

P	Q	$P * Q$
T	T	F
T	F	F
F	T	F
F	F	T

Chapter 4

THE DEEPER STRUCTURE

OF STATEMENTS

4-1 QUANTIFIERS

Consider the statement:

> For each x, if x is a real number, and x is greater than zero, then, for some y, y is a real number and $y^2 = x^2$.

This complex statement cannot be broken down in the manner used in the preceding sections. We can perceive conjunctions and conditionals within the statement, but they are cemented together by the phrases "for each x" and "for some y." If the given statement occurred as a component of a still more complex one, *the given statement would have to be treated as a unit in any truth-table analysis.*

The modifying phrase "for each x" (or any linguistic equivalent) is called a **universal quantifier**; the phrase "for some x" (or any linguistic equivalent) is called an **existential quantifier**. Quantifiers play a fundamental role in mathematical reasoning. Since we shall need rules for dealing with quantifiers, special symbols to state those rules will be convenient. We shall adopt $\forall x$ for the universal quantifier, and $\exists x$ for the existential quantifier. The inverted A can be associated with the word "all," and the reversed E with the word "exists." Of course, other letters may be used in place of x or y. We shall also adopt the convention that the scope of each quantifier is just the first statement, sentential variable, or sentential formula lying to the right of the quantifier. In particular, if a left bracket immediately follows a quantifier, the scope of that quantifier is indicated by the pair of brackets. Thus we shall write $\exists x P \lor Q$ for $[\exists x P] \lor Q$. If we had wanted the quantifier to apply to the whole disjunction, we would have written $\exists x [P \lor Q]$.

In a formula such as $\forall y \exists x P$, the statement to the right of $\forall y$ is $\exists x P$, so the whole formula must be interpreted as $\forall y [\exists x P]$. A tilde preceding a quantifier negates just the quantified statement. Thus we shall write $\sim \forall x P \lor Q$ for $[\sim[\forall x P]] \lor Q$; $\sim \exists x \forall y P \Rightarrow Q$ for $[\sim[\exists x[\forall y P]]] \Rightarrow Q$; and so on.

It should be emphasized that $\exists x P$ asserts the existence of *at least one* value of x such that P holds; there may be many such values. Linguistic equivalents of "for some x" include "for at least one x," "there is an x such that," and "there exists an x such that." Other verbalizations of $\forall x$ include "for all x" and "for any x." Even though some of these verbalizations appear to include a statement such as "there is an x," *a quantifier must never be counted as a substatement.*

The two quantifiers are related in meaning. In talking about hats, "Every hat here costs at least ten dollars" has the same meaning as "There is no hat here that costs less than ten dollars." In talking about cats, "In the dark, all cats are gray" means the same as "In the dark, there is no cat that is not gray." If P is true for every x, then there is no x for which P is false. Hence $\forall x P$ should be interchangeable with $\sim \exists x \sim P$, and we shall take the latter as the definition of the former, thus leaving $\exists x$ as the sole basic quantifier.

Definition

$$\forall x P \quad \text{for} \quad \sim \exists x \sim P$$

One more abbreviation, for strings of quantifiers of the same kind, will be found to be rather convenient.

Definitions

$$\forall xy P \quad \text{for} \quad \forall x \forall y P$$

$$\forall xyz P \quad \text{for} \quad \forall x \forall y \forall z P \quad \text{and so on}$$

$$\exists xy P \quad \text{for} \quad \exists x \exists y P$$

$$\exists xyz P \quad \text{for} \quad \exists x \exists y \exists z P \quad \text{and so on}$$

Although from the standpoint of meaning, a statement of the form $\exists xy P$ is clearly equivalent to one of the form $\exists yx P$, we shall *prove* later that each is substitutable for the other, and likewise for the pair $\forall xy P$ and $\forall yx P$. Until we do prove this, we shall treat them as disparate forms.

Beware of permuting existential with universal quantifiers! It is easy to find a statement P for which $\forall x \exists y P$ is true but $\exists y \forall x P$ is false. For example, taking P as $x > y$, it is true that, in the real numbers, for each x there is at least one y such that $x > y$, but there is no y such that every x is greater than that y. On the other hand, we shall prove that whenever any statement of the form $\exists x \forall y P$ is true, then so is $\forall y \exists x P$.

EXERCISES

Rewrite each formula with a minimum number of brackets, making use of the scope conventions and abbreviated forms like $\forall x y$.

1. $\sim [\forall x [\exists y [P \Rightarrow [\forall z [\sim Q]]]]]$

2. $\exists z [P \Leftrightarrow [\forall x [\forall y Q] \vee [\sim [R \wedge S]]]]$

3. $\forall x [\sim [\forall y [P \vee Q]]]$

4. $\exists x [\exists y [R \vee [\forall t [[\forall z P] \vee Q]]]]$

In Exercises 5 through 8, rewrite each formula so that no scope convention or abbreviated quantifier is used.

5. $\forall x y P \vee \exists x Q \Rightarrow \forall y R \wedge S$

6. $\exists x [\forall y P \Rightarrow \sim \forall z Q \Rightarrow R]$

7. $\sim \exists y \forall x t [Q \vee R] \wedge [\forall z P \Rightarrow S]$

8. $\forall x y z [P \vee \forall t Q \Rightarrow \exists w P \vee S]$

9. Find two pairs of nonmathematical statements of the form $\forall x \exists y P$—$\exists y \forall x P$, in which the first one is true and the second one false.

10. Find two pairs of nonmathematical statements of the form $\forall x P$—$\forall x \sim P$, showing that both statements of such a pair can be false. What about $\exists x P$ and $\exists x \sim P$ in these cases?

11. **(a)** Accepting for the moment that $\sim [\sim Q]$ may be substituted for any statement Q, find three more relationships between the quantifiers like the definition of $\forall x P$.

(b) What connection can you find between (a) and the previous exercise?

4-2 THE SIGNIFICANCE OF QUANTIFIERS

It was stated that quantifiers play a fundamental role in mathematical reasoning. Let us consider a familiar theorem:

Base angles of an isosceles triangle are congruent.

In the proof, we "take" a triangle abc† and assume that two sides, say $\overline{ab}$ and $\overline{ac}$, are congruent. We then deduce that angle abc is congruent to angle acb. When we are done, it would seem that we have proved the statement:

If abc is a triangle with $\overline{ab} \cong \overline{ac}$, then $\sphericalangle abc \cong \sphericalangle acb$.

If this really is a statement of the theorem, do we have the right to apply it later to a triangle named pqr? We have that right only if abc was a sufficiently general triangle. If we wish to be explicit about the generality of the theorem we could start its statement thus:

For any noncollinear points a, b, c, if abc . . . .

We could then have a rule allowing us to apply the theorem to three points named p, q, and r.

One might think that a way out would be to agree that theorems are always general statements, and to allow changes of letters with proper discretion, thus dispensing with the universal quantifier. This only brings up a new question: How do we know that we have proved a theorem in sufficient generality to allow subsequent application to other situations? By insisting upon explicit use of quantifiers, we can provide for rules under which quantifiers may be safely prefixed to statements in the course of a proof, and other rules allowing application of a generalized statement to a particular case.

As another example of the indispensability of quantifiers, let us suppose that we find a student asserting as a law‡ of algebra that

$$(x + 3)^2 = x^2 + 3^2$$

---

† We are using small letters for points rather than the familiar capitals, to agree with the convention for variables that we shall adopt in § 4-5.

‡ This is one application of a favorite student principle, the *law of universal linearity.* Other applications frequently seen are

$$\frac{a}{b + c} = \frac{a}{b} + \frac{a}{c}, \quad \text{and} \quad \sin 2x = 2 \sin x$$

We might like to show that his law is false, by showing that its negation is true. However, the negation of that statement *as given* is

$$(x + 3)^2 \neq x^2 + 3^2$$

which is no better as a general statement. The statement that we need to prove is

$$\exists x[(x + 3)^2 \neq x^2 + 3^2]$$

which is the correct negation of

$$\forall x[(x + 3)^2 = x^2 + 3^2]$$

as one can see from the definition of $\forall xP$.

4-3 PURIFYING QUANTIFIERS

Let us consider the statement:

There exists an x greater than zero, such that for every real number y, $xy = y$.

Here the clause "There exists an x greater than zero" is not a pure quantifier, for it has been loaded with properties of x. Similarly, the phrase "for every real number y" contains a description which is not properly a part of a universal quantifier. For amenability to our rules, such loaded quantifying phrases and clauses will have to be "purified." With a pure quantifier, the first clause would start

There exists an x such that . . .

To retain the original content, we would then continue

x is greater than zero and . . .

In general, a statement of the form

There is an x with property p such that . . .

can be converted to a statement of the form

> There is an x such that x has property p and . . .

The rest of the original statement would start (using a pure quantifier)

> for every y . . .

We include the information about the nature of y by continuing

> if y is a real number, then . . .

In general a statement of the form

> For every x with property p . . .

can be converted to a statement of the form

> For every x, if x has property p, then . . .

A modified universal quantifier leads to a universal quantifier followed by a conditional, when purified. A modified existential quantifier leads to an existential quantifier followed by a conjunction, when purified.

In converting a colloquial statement to symbols, there will usually be some latitude as to choice of structure, particularly when purifying quantifiers. Let us consider the following statement:

> For any three distinct noncollinear points, there do not exist two distinct planes containing all of them.

We shall start with $\forall xyz$, of course, but in what form do we present the fact that x, y, and z are distinct noncollinear points? Legally, we could choose one sentential variable for the whole description.

> P: x, y, and z are distinct noncollinear points.

Similarly, we could let Q carry the rest of the burden.

> Q: m and n are distinct planes containing x, y, and z.

Then our statement takes the form

> (1) $\forall xyz[P \Rightarrow \sim\exists mnQ]$

This is not very illuminating; too much structure has been concealed. Statements P and Q each contain several items of possibly useful information. Let us start with P.

P_1: x, y, and z are points.
P_2: x, y, and z are distinct.
P_3: x, y, and z are collinear.

(We prefer positive statements for sentential variables.)

Even this can be improved. In the course of a proof, we would probably want to use the properties of pointhood separately for each point.

$P_{1.1}$: x is a point.
$P_{1.2}$: y is a point.
$P_{1.3}$: z is a point.

In breaking down P_2, do not fall into the trap of saying "x is distinct!" Distinctness is a relation, the negation of equality. If we wish to refine P_2, we should do it as follows:

$P_{2.1}$: $x = y$
$P_{2.2}$: $y = z$
$P_{2.3}$: $z = x$

We shall leave P_3 alone; the possibility of refinement depends too much upon how collinearity has been defined. It might even be an undefined relation. Proceeding in the same manner with Q, we can produce nine substatements.

$Q_{1.1}$: m is a plane.
$Q_{1.2}$: n is a plane.
Q_2 : $m = n$.
$Q_{3.1}$: $x \in m$.
$Q_{3.2}$: $y \in m$.
$Q_{3.3}$: $z \in m$.
$Q_{4.1}$: $x \in n$.
$Q_{4.2}$: $y \in n$.
$Q_{4.3}$: $z \in n$.

Our formula now is:

$$(2) \quad \forall xyz[P_{1.1} \wedge P_{1.2} \wedge P_{1.3} \wedge \sim P_{2.1} \wedge \sim P_{2.2} \wedge \sim P_{2.3} \wedge P_3 \Rightarrow$$
$$\sim\exists mn[Q_{1.1} \wedge Q_{1.2} \wedge \sim Q_2 \wedge Q_{3.1} \wedge Q_{3.2} \wedge Q_{3.3} \wedge Q_{4.1} \wedge Q_{4.2} \wedge Q_{4.3}]]$$

Formula (1) is one extreme; formula (2) is, perhaps, the other. In a particular proof you might be able to use something between the two. For example, one would seldom split "x is a real number" into "x is a number" and "x is real" in a statement such as that of Exercise 1 below.

EXERCISES

Provide a dictionary and write a formula for each statement, breaking the information down into useful substatements as described in the preceding section. If you feel vague in your mind as to the mathematical meaning of some of the terms, remember that only logical form matters.

1. For every positive real number s there are two distinct real numbers q and r each of whose squares is equal to s.

2. For any pair of distinct points a and b there is a third point c such that $\overline{ac} \simeq \overline{bc}$.

3. There exist two distinct vectors e and f such that whenever† $ae + bf = \theta$, then $a = 0$ and $b = 0$.

4. For any x_0 in the interval (a, b), $f(x_0)$ is defined, and $\lim\limits_{x \to x_0} f(x) = f(x_0)$. [This is a definition of "f is continuous over the interval (a, b)."]

5. For any x_0 in the interval (a, b),

$$\lim_{h \to 0} \frac{f(x_0 + h) - f(x_0)}{h}$$

exists. (There should be an existential quantifier in this one.)

6. For any $h > 0$ there exists a $k > 0$ such that whenever† $0 < |x - a| < k$, then $|f(x) - L| < k$.

7. There is one and only one y such that $f(x_0) = y$. (This a definition of "f is defined at x_0.")

---

† "Whenever" always connotes universal quantification, which is not the case with "when."

8. For every transcendental garf k, there are two distinct paradoxical frugals r and s such that k transfixes $r \diamond s$.

Each of the statements in Exercises 9 through 16 is a postulate or a theorem in its respective system. As such, it should have every variable (letter) covered by a quantifier. First rewrite each statement so that the quantification is explicit. It will be necessary to revise some of them considerably to introduce quantifiable variables. Then provide a dictionary for each and write a formula. You may assume that the usual terms of the relevant systems (such as $\triangle abc$) are available.

9. If $x < y$, there is a z such that $x < z$ and $z < y$.

10. If $a < b$, and $0 < x$, then $ax < bx$.

11. Two distinct lines have a point in common. (Start "For every m and n, if m is a line and n is a line . . . .")

12. Every angle has a bisector.

13. In a right triangle, the square of the hypotenuse equals the sum of the squares of the other two sides. (Start "$\forall abc$ . . . .")

14. $x^n + y^n = z^n$ has no solution in positive integers, if n is an integer greater than 2. (The most famous undecided conjecture in all of mathematics.)

15. There is no greatest prime integer. (Try to do this using $>$, but not "greatest.")

16. There is no rational number whose square equals 2.

4-4 ATOMIC STATEMENTS

At this point we must go still more deeply into the structure of mathematical statements. By an **atomic statement** we shall mean one that is not built up from other statements by quantifiers and sentential operators. In a formal mathematical system, a typical atomic statement frequently consists of two substantive expressions denoting mathematical objects, one on each side of a connecting symbol. For example, the statements

(1) $2 + 3 = 5$

(2) $a \subseteq \{x \mid x \in b \lor x \in c\}$

(3) $n^2 > \sum_{i < n} i$

are atomic statements. The connecting symbol, $=$, $\subseteq$, and $>$, in each of these examples has the force of a verb expressing a relation between the objects named. In verbalizing these statements, we may find the "verbs" turning into phrases that include prepositions, adjectives, or other parts of speech. The symbol $\subseteq$ becomes "is contained in" or "is a subset of"; the symbol $>$ becomes "is greater than"; and so on. Whether or not the connecting symbol can be expressed by a single word is a matter of linguistic chance; although it takes at least three words to verbalize $\subseteq$, the inverse relation $\supseteq$ is usually verbalized by the single word "contains." (If anyone insists on a one-word verbalization of the symbol $>$, you can offer him "exceeds.")

Looking at the situation from the other end, we find that informal mathematical discourse may require a considerable amount of revision in the course of converting it to our high-powered symbols. One of the uses of the language of sets is to facilitate such restructuring by the substitution of substantive expressions in the place of descriptions. For example, we may write $x \in R^+$ for "x is a rational number greater than zero"—R^+ having been previously defined as the collection of all rational numbers greater than zero.

An atomic statement may contain recognizable statements within it. For example, statement (2) above contains a compound statement formed from two atomic statements, $x \in b \lor x \in c$. However, that compound statement has been used to build the substantive expression to the right of $\subseteq$, and the whole statement cannot be broken down into just substatements, sentential operators, and quantifiers. Thus a list of all the atomic statements to be seen in statement (2) would consist of three statements: $x \in b$, $x \in c$, and statement (2) itself. Similarly, $i < n$ is a statement used to build the substantive expression to the right of $>$ in statement (3), but the whole statement must also be classed as atomic.

EXERCISES

List all the atomic statements to be seen in each of the following exercises.

1. $\forall x[x > 0 \Rightarrow \exists y[y < x \wedge y^2 > 0]]$

2. $\forall ab[a \neq b \Rightarrow \exists c[\overline{ac} \cong \overline{cb}]]$

3. $\forall a[a = \{x \mid x \in a\}]$

4. $\forall x[x \in a \cup b \Rightarrow x \in b] \Leftrightarrow a \subseteq b$

5. $\forall y[y \in \{x \mid x > 0\} \Rightarrow \exists z[z \in \{x \mid x < 0\} \wedge z^2 < y]]$

6. $\forall n\left[n + \sum_{i<n} i = \sum_{i \leq n} i\right]$

4-5 TERMS

Any substantive expression representing a specific or nonspecific object of a mathematical system we shall call a **term** of that system. The kind of atomic sentence illustrated in the preceding section thus consists of two terms and a verbal connective. Just as statements can be used to construct more complex statements, so can terms be used to build terms. In arithmetic, 3 is a term which enters into the structure of the term "2 + 3." In the language of sets, b is a term in the statement "$x \in b \vee x \in c$," which, in turn, is part of the term $\{x \mid x \in b \vee x \in c\}$. On the intuitional level, a term is distinguished by its linguistic use as a substantive. In §§ 10-2 and 10-3 we shall give more formal criteria for determining whether or not a given formula is a term. For the time being, the only specific term forms we need to consider are the pure variables; more complex terms will be found only in exercises and in illustrative examples, where you may rely on your familiarity with the mathematical meanings.

We shall be discussing the use in statements of terms in a general sort of way, and variables in particular. We now choose the Greek letters α and β to represent terms in general, and lowercase Latin letters for discussing the use of a variable as a term.

There are three kinds of occurrence of a variable that we must exclude from consideration as terms: those found in the quantifiers $\forall x$ and $\exists x$, and to the left of the line in the set notation $\{x \mid \cdots\}$. In fact, when we speak of "occurrences of x," such uses will never be included.

EXERCISES

List all the different terms you can find in each of the following statements. Assume natural contexts for each.

1. $\forall x[2 + y < 3 + y]$

2. $\forall abc[\overline{ab} \simeq \overline{bc} \Rightarrow \sphericalangle bac \simeq \sphericalangle bca]$

3. $\{x \mid x \in a \lor x \in b\} = \{y \mid y \in a \lor y \in b\}$

4. $\{x \mid 2 + 2 = 5\} = \varnothing$

5. $A = \pi r^2$

6. $n + \sum\limits_{i<n} i = \sum\limits_{i \leq n} i$

7. $\forall mn[m \parallel n \Rightarrow m \cap n = \varnothing]$

8. $\forall x[(x + iy)^2 = (x^2 - y^2) + 2ixy]$

4-6 CONSTANTS AND VARIABLES

Let us now turn our attention to the uses made of individual letters, or other simple symbols, as terms in a mathematical statement. Such uses are of three kinds:

1. To denote any one of a class of mathematical objects, as in the sentence "For every x, $x^2 > 0$."

2. To denote a supposedly fixed, but unspecified object, as in the algebraic solution of a verbal problem, when we "let x be the number of dollars Professor R lost at Las Vegas."

3. To denote a reasonably well-defined unique mathematical object, as exemplified by the numerals, or by the use of e to denote the base of the natural logarithms, or by the use of R to represent the set of rational numbers.

One may say that these uses correspond to the notions of variable, unknown, and constant, respectively. However, these notions are themselves inexact, and so are the corresponding descriptions of the uses. There is no sharp method of distinguishing among them in that formulation. For example, when we say, "The graph of $2x + 3y = 5$ is a straight line," the x and y in the equation are apparently variables. But suppose that we continue "and the graph of $3x + 2y = 5$ is also a straight line. The point $x = 1$, $y = 1$, is the point of intersection of these two lines, and hence represents the simultaneous solution of the two equations." Now the two variables appear as unknowns, particularly if the equations arose out of a verbal problem. For another example, consider the statement, "The graph of an equation of the form $ax + by = c$ is a straight line, if a and b are not both zero." Are a, b, and c constants here in the sense of the third use described above?

In this text "constant" will be restricted to mean a primitive symbol that represents a unique mathematical object. Its uniqueness may be postulated, or the uniqueness may be established by a theorem. Sometimes we temporarily assume the existence of a certain unique mathematical object, perhaps even to show that such an object does not exist! For example, in the classical proof that there is no rational number whose square is 2, we show that the assumption that there is such a rational number leads to a contradiction. We start out, "Let r be a rational number such that $r^2 = 2$." This looks as though the r should be classed as a constant. We shall class it as a variable, reserving "constant" to describe symbols that represent *demonstrably* unique objects.

Any particular symbol can be a constant in one context and a variable in another, or it may be used to represent one unique object in one system and a different one in another. For example, π is a constant in any branch of mathematics that deals with the real numbers, but in classical number theory it is frequently used to designate an unspecified prime integer, and is then a variable. Similarly, 0 may be used as the name of the empty set (in set theory), or the name of the identity element of an abelian group (in modern algebra), or the name of the minimum element of a partially ordered set (in lattice theory). However, once a letter or other symbol has been used as a constant in a particular presentation of a particular system, it is reserved thenceforth in that presentation as an official name for the mathematical object concerned.

Any lowercase Latin letter that occurs as a term and is not a constant will be called a variable in this text. (This use of "variable" does not include sentential variables or the predicate variables to be introduced in § 4-8.) Instead of trying to distinguish between "variables" and "unknowns" we shall consider "bound variables" and "free variables," a dichotomy which approximates the other one but can be formally determined in certain situations that will be of interest to us.

4-7 BOUND VARIABLES AND FREE VARIABLES

Our first concern will be the classification of variables as bound or free, as they occur within terms. Variables are used to build complex terms in a great variety of ways. Here are some samples:

(1) $\{f \mid f$ is a continuous function over $[a, b]\}$.

(2) $\lim_{t \to x} tx$

(3) $\sum_{i=1}^{i=n} i^2$

(4) The graph of $x^2 + y^2 = r^2$.

Once more we depart from a formalistic program for our criteria. If the term as a whole cannot be evaluated without assigning a value (not necessarily numerical) to the variable; if, in some sense, the meaning of the term is a function of the meaning of the variable, then the occurrence of the variable is free in the term. If, on the other hand, one cannot meaningfully assign any value to the variable, then the occurrence of the variable within the term is bound. In (1) the second f is bound (the first f is not a term), and a and b are free. In (2) t is bound and x is free. In (3) i is bound and n is free. In (4) x and y are bound and r is free.

We are baldly appealing to meaning here, but, again, the decision as to whether a variable is bound or free within a term will be called for only in applying the logic, or in illustrative examples. We bring it in at this point mainly to help you develop some feeling for what lies behind certain rules of logic. In Chapter 10 you will find a more formal approach to the problem.

There is another way in which a variable becomes bound, which has a more obvious connection with our rules. Any x occurring in a statement P

is bound in $\exists x P$ and in $\forall x P$. That is, the quantifiers bind their named variables in any statement within their scope. (We remind you that the x in the quantifier itself is not counted as an occurrence of a variable of either kind.) Here the relation of "free variable" to "unknown" is a little plainer. In the statement "For each x, $x^2 > t$," the t is free and the x is bound. The feeling of the sentence is that the user is talking about a particular number t, to which a whole class of other numbers (the x's) have a certain relation. One can also take the position that the sentence discusses the relation of the universe of discourse (the real numbers, in this case) to an unspecified member t. This is true even in a statement such as "There is an x such that $x < z$," although at first glance it may seem as though a particular x has been selected. The selection, however, does not take place until and unless we follow up with "Let w be such a number," which amounts to removing the quantifier and choosing a particular free variable. There will be special provision for this kind of step, as well as one for removing universal quantifiers.

If a variable, say x, occurs free in a given term, but that term is used in a statement within the scope of an x-quantifier, then the occurrence of x in the statement as a whole is bound. In the statement

$$\forall x \left[\lim_{t \to x} tx = x^2 \right]$$

x is bound, as well as t.

All free occurrences of a given variable are understood to represent the same thing throughout a proof, but bound occurrences need not have any connection with each other except where bound by the same quantifier. We may have a statement like

$$\forall x [x^2 \geq 0] \Rightarrow \forall xy [x^2 + y^2 \geq 2xy]$$

without any need of matching values of x in the antecedent with those in the consequent. However, the x in $x^2 + y^2$ and the x in $2xy$ are understood to be identical. Thus we cannot claim that $\forall xy [x^2 + y^2 \geq 2xy]$ is false just because $1^2 + 3^2 \ngeq 2 \times 5 \times 3$.

EXERCISES

For each of the statements in the exercises of § 4-5, list the constants, bound variables, and free variables.

4-8 PREDICATE NOTATION

Intuitively,

      (1) $\forall x[y < x^2]$

and   (2) $\forall z[y < z^2]$

have the same meanings, and we should allow interchanges between such pairs. However,

      (3) $\forall y[y < y^2]$

is quite different from the first two in content. If the variables are restricted to real numbers, then (1) and (2) are true whenever the (free) variable y represents a negative number, but (3) is false as it stands. To facilitate discussion of statements related as these are, we shall use a notation similar to that of ordinary functions. In this notation, statements are represented by forms such as $P(x)$, $Q(3 + y)$, and $R(3, y)$. Here the capital letters are thought of as representing a predicate, that is, that which is asserted about the terms listed within the parentheses. We shall call the capital letters so used **predicate variables**; they may be distinguished from sentential variables by the parentheses that follow them and contain one or more terms. The terms are separated by commas if there is more than one. As shown above, P and Q are each followed by parentheses containing a single term. In this case, we refer to P and Q as **one-place predicate variables**. On the other hand, R appears above as a **two-place predicate variable**, since there are two separate terms, 3 and y, within its parentheses. A complete string—predicate variable, parentheses, and term(s)—represents a statement, just as a sentential variable does. However, the notation permits us to say more about manipulations with that statement, for we can go still further with the analogy to the traditional notation for functions. Consider the following three statements:

      (4) $\exists z[x = t + z]$

      (5) $\exists z[y = t + z]$

      (6) $\exists z[4 + \pi = t + z]$

If we used $P(x)$ to represent (4), then we could use $P(y)$ for (5), and $P(4 + \pi)$ for (6).

Notice that we can use a one-place predicate variable, $P(x)$, for (4), although there are three (numerical) variables occurring in it. At our convenience, we could also have used $Q(t)$, or $R(x, t)$, but we would not ordinarily use $U(z)$, $S(x, z)$, or $T(x, t, z)$, for we are going to avoid mention of a variable within the parentheses unless it occurs free within the statement covered by the predicate variable. However, if that statement occurs as part of a larger statement, in such a way that it is covered by a quantifier, a mentioned variable may be bound in the larger context. Thus, if we adopt $R(x, t)$ for $\exists z[x = t + z]$, we may then represent $\forall x \exists z[x = t + z]$ by $\forall x R(x, t)$, although the x in $R(x, t)$ is now bound. In turn, we would not use, say, $W(x, t)$ for $\forall x \exists z[x = t + z]$, but we might represent that statement by $W(t)$. A still more complex statement such as $\exists t \forall x \exists z[x = t + z]$ could then be represented by $\exists t W(t)$ or by $\exists t \forall x R(x, t)$. The freedom of choice between $P(x)$ and $R(x, t)$ to represent (4) illustrates that if a variable is not named in the parentheses, one must not therefore assume that the variable does not occur free in the statement.

If we simply follow out the idea of substitution already used to obtain $P(y)$ and $P(y + 4)$, then $P(z)$ would turn out as

$$(7) \quad \exists z[z = t + z]$$

and $P(t)$ would be

$$(8) \quad \exists z[t = t + z]$$

Statements (7) and (8) represent a change from (4) that goes further than merely saying the same thing about something with a different name. In using the same predicate variable more than once in the same context, we shall restrict the notation in the next section so that in a context where (4) is referred to as $P(x)$, (7) would not be referred to as $P(z)$, nor (8) as $P(t)$.

EXERCISES

1. Formula (2) in § 4-3 can be written with just five predicate variables.†
  Provide a dictionary and do so.

† The remarks in the footnote to Exercises 17 through 26 of §-2-7 with regard to sentential variables and sentential "constants" apply here to predicate variables and "constants" as well.

2. (a) Using $Q(x, y)$ for $x = y$, how would you write "x, y, and z are distinct"?

(b) How about "x, y, z, and t are distinct"?

The dictionaries given in Exercises 3 through 15 are cumulative. Only new predicates are given for each exercise; you should use the ones given in preceding exercises when you need them. Without inventing predicates, and without leaving any substatements in nonpredicate form, write a formula for each statement.

3. For every x and y, if $x > y$, there is a z such that $x > z$ and $z > y$.
Dictionary: $G(x, y)$: $x > y$.

4. For every x and y and any positive z, if $x > y$, then $xz > yz$. (Use a suitable definition of "positive.")

5. The product of any two real numbers is zero if and only if one of them is zero.
Dictionary: $R(x)$: x is a real number.
　　　　　　$Q(x, y)$: $x = y$.

6. For any real numbers x and y with x not zero, there is a real number z such that $xz = y$.

7. Whenever real numbers x and y are distinct, then $x > y$ or $y > x$, and conversely.

8. There exist two distinct vectors e and f such that whenever $xe + yf = 0$, then x and y are both zero.
Dictionary: $W(x)$: x is a vector.

9. For any real numbers x and y, and any vectors e and f, $xe + yf$ is a vector.

10. Any vectors e, f, and g are linearly dependent if and only if there are real numbers x, y, and z, not all zero, such that $xe + yf + zg = 0$.
Dictionary: $D(x, y, z)$: x, y, and z are linearly dependent.

11. There is a rational number between every pair of distinct real numbers.
Dictionary: $T(x)$: x is a rational number.

12. There is no rational number whose square is 2.

13. There is no greatest prime integer.
  Dictionary: $P(x)$: x is a prime integer.

14. Whenever f and g are continuous functions on $[0, 1]$, then so are $f + g$ and fg, and, provided $f(x)$ is never zero for any x in $[0, 1]$, f/g is also.
  Dictionary: $C(x, y, z)$: x is a continuous function on $[y, z]$.
  $B(x, y, z)$: x is in $[y, z]$.

15. Any function f continuous on $[a, b]$ attains its maximum there. (If you can express this without inventing a predicate, you have really caught on!)

16. If we use $\exists_1 x \cdots$ to represent "There exists one and only one x such that . . . ," write a definition of $\exists_1 x P(x)$ in terms of the usual quantifiers, the predicate variable P, and $=$.

17. The principle of finite induction can be approximately given by:
  If we have a statement about the positive integer n, which is true for $n = 1$, and which is true for $k + 1$ whenever it is true for k, then the statement is true for every positive integer.
  Restate this precisely, using $P(n)$ for the statement under discussion, and assuming a universe of positive integers.

18. What are the significant differences in meaning among statements (4), (7), and (8) in the text?

19. (a) Assign a meaning to $P(x, y)$ such that $\forall xy[P(x, y) \Rightarrow P(y, x)]$ is true.
  (b) Assign a meaning to $P(x, y)$ such that $\forall xy[P(x, y) \Rightarrow \sim P(y, x)]$ is true.

4-9 SPECIAL PAIRS OF STATEMENT FORMS

In Chapter 5 we shall, at last, get around to giving our ten rules of logic. Five of these will deal with pairs of statements that can be represented by formulas using identical predicate variables. Two of the five (*Choice* and *Generalization*) will concern pairs of statements that differ, at most, in the use of one variable instead of another, as with statements (4) and (5) of § 4-8. For these two rules we need the definition of $P(x)$—$P(y)$ pairs given below. Two other rules (*Instance* and *Example*) will involve substituting a more general kind of term for a variable, as in the pair of statements (4) and (7) in § 4-8. For these rules, we shall define $P(x)$—$P(\alpha)$ pairs. Finally, one rule involves the general substitution of terms, based on equality (*Equality Substitution*), for which we shall define $P(\alpha)$—$P(\beta)$ pairs.

$P(x)$—$P(y)$ Pairs

$P(x)$—$P(y)$ will represent a pair of statements, each of which may be formed from the other by *complete* replacement of the free occurrences of one variable by (free) occurrences of the other. If either variable represents an element of a restricted class by notational convention, then the other variable must be one which is restricted to the same class.

The following is a $P(x)$—$P(y)$ pair:

(1) $\exists z[x + z = 0]$　　　$\exists z[y + z = 0]$

The next is a $P(y)$—$P(z)$ pair:

(2) $y + 2 = 3y$　　　$z + 2 = 3z$

The next three are *not* $P(x)$—$P(y)$ pairs for the reasons given.

(3) $x + 3 = 3y$　　　$y + 3 = 3y$

(Incomplete substitution of x for y.)

(4) $\exists y[x = t + z]$　　　$\exists y[y = t + z]$

(Substituted y not free in second statement, hence improper substitution of x for y.)

(5) $\forall y[y + 1 > y]$　　　$\forall x[x + 1 > x]$

(Change in quantifier, x and y not free.)

$P(x)$—$P(\alpha)$ Pairs

$P(x)$—$P(\alpha)$ will represent a pair of statements satisfying the following requirements:

(a) x is a variable, α represents a term.
(b) If the variable represents an element of a restricted class by notational convention, then the term α must represent an element of that class.
(c) $P(\alpha)$ can be obtained by substituting α for every free occurrence of x in $P(x)$.

The following is a $P(x)$—$P(\alpha)$ pair, with $\alpha = 25$:

$$(6)\ \exists z[x + z = 0] \qquad \exists z[25 + z = 0]$$

The next is a $P(z)$—$P(\alpha)$ pair, with $\alpha = x + y$.

$$(7)\ \forall x[z + x^2 + t > z] \qquad \forall x[(x + y) + x^2 + t > (x + y)]$$

In (7), the x that was free in $x + y$ happened to become bound by the substitution of that term for z. This is permissible in a $P(x)$—$P(\alpha)$ pair. Note also that the pair in (1) fits the requirements for a $P(x)$—$P(\alpha)$ pair, with $\alpha = y$, and also for a $P(y)$—$P(\alpha)$ pair (in reversed order) with $\alpha = x$. This is always true of a $P(x)$—$P(y)$ pair, and, in that sense, the requirements for a $P(x)$—$P(y)$ pair are symmetric, and stronger than those for a $P(x)$—$P(\alpha)$ pair. Give particular notice to the pair (4). It is a $P(x)$—$P(\alpha)$ pair, with $\alpha = y$, but it is not a $P(x)$—$P(y)$ pair, illustrating how the notation agreements can carry out the promise of the last paragraph of § 4-8.

$P(\alpha)$—$P(\beta)$ Pairs

$P(\alpha)$—$P(\beta)$ will represent a pair of statements for which a third statement $P(z)$ can be found forming $P(z)$—$P(\alpha)$ and $P(z)$—$P(\beta)$ pairs with the given statements. [The $P(z)$ will not be uniquely determined in many cases.]

The following is a $P(\alpha)$—$P(\beta)$ pair:

$$(8)\ y^3 + x = y^2 \qquad x^2 + x = y^2$$

$P(z)$ could be $z + x = y^2$, with $\alpha = y^3$ and $\beta = x^2$. $P(z)$ could also be $z = y^2$, with $\alpha = y^3 + x$, and $\beta = x^2 + x$.

Another $P(\alpha)$—$P(\beta)$ pair:

$$(9)\ \forall x \exists y[x + y = z] \qquad \forall x \exists y[y + x = z]$$

Here we cannot talk about $P(z)$ as the third statement; we must always choose a new free variable in analyzing $P(\alpha)$—$P(\beta)$ pairs. If we let $P(t)$ be $\forall x \exists y[t = z]$, then with $\alpha = x + y$ and $\beta = y + x$, we have the necessary pattern.

$P(\alpha)$—$P(\beta)$ are symmetric, like $P(x)$—$P(y)$ pairs, and every $P(x)$—$P(\alpha)$ pair is a $P(\beta)$—$P(\alpha)$ pair, with $x = \beta$. A fortiori, every $P(x)$—$P(y)$ pair is a $P(\alpha)$—$P(\beta)$ pair.

*   *   *

We have tried to indicate by the given examples that x and y are to be taken as representative; any other lowercase Latin letters may replace them in the definitions. In the first classification, the variables do not even have to be distinct; two identical statements comprise such a pair, provided there is at least one occurrence of a free variable. [This proviso is called for only because we agreed, in § 4-8, that the use of $P(x)$ would imply a free occurrence of x. It will do no particular harm if we allow identical pairs of statements to be included in all three classes, *even when no free variables are present.*]

The symmetries and asymmetries of the three classes are shown below.

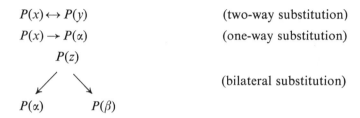

$$P(x) \leftrightarrow P(y) \qquad\qquad \text{(two-way substitution)}$$
$$P(x) \rightarrow P(\alpha) \qquad\qquad \text{(one-way substitution)}$$

$$P(z)$$

(bilateral substitution)

$$P(\alpha) \qquad\qquad P(\beta)$$

EXERCISES

For each of the pairs of statements in Exercises 1 through 12,
(a) Classify it as a $P(x)$—$P(y)$, $P(x)$—$P(\alpha)$, or $P(\alpha)$—$P(\beta)$ pair. Give the strongest classification, and use other variables where appropriate. At least one pair does not fit any of the three classifications.
(b) If the pair is not of the first classification, give the α or β involved.
(c) If the pair is a $P(\alpha)$—$P(\beta)$ pair, give the corresponding $P(z)$ you have selected.

1. $x + 2 = z$ $x + 2 = y$

2. $x + x = 3z$ $y + x = 3z$

3. $\exists x[1 = x^2 + y]$ $\exists x[1 = x^2 + y + 2]$

4. $\forall c[a \cup b \subseteq c]$ $\forall d[a \cup b \subseteq d]$

5. $x + x^2 = y^2$ $y + x^2 = y^2$

6. $\forall z[zy = x + z]$ $\forall z[z = x + z]$

7. $\exists x[x > 0 \wedge \forall z[x < x^2 + z^2]]$ $\qquad$ $\exists x[x > 0 \wedge \forall z[y < x^2 + z^2]]$

8. $\int_1^t f(x)\, dx = 0$ $\qquad$ $\int_1^u f(x)\, dx = 0$

9. $x = 5 + y$ $\qquad$ $y = 5 + x$

10. $\forall x[x^2 > 0] \Rightarrow \forall y[(x + y)^2 > 0]$ $\qquad$ $\forall x[x^2 > 0]$
$\qquad\qquad\qquad\qquad\qquad\qquad\qquad\qquad \Rightarrow \forall y[(x + y)^2 > 0]$

11. $\forall x[x^2 > 0] \Rightarrow (x - y)^2 > 0$ $\qquad$ $\forall x[x^2 > 0] \Rightarrow (t - x)^2 > 0$

12. $\exists xy[x + y = 0]$ $\qquad$ $\exists xy[x + x = 0]$

13. Show how the pair of identical statements $2 + 2 = 4$ and $2 + 2 = 4$ can be considered a $P(\alpha)$—$P(\beta)$ pair.

14. Give a plausible definition of a $P(x, y)$—$P(w, t)$ pair.

Chapter 5

THE DEMONSTRATION

5-1 INTRODUCTION

As described in § 1-7, a formal mathematical system Σ is determined by

a given collection of undefined expressions,
a set of rules for forming statements, and
a set of statements called postulates and definitions.

The rules for forming statements permit the construction of a limitless number of statements. Some of these are *provable* (to be defined in § 5-8) and in the context of the system Σ, we call them "true" statements. The negation of a provable statement is called "disprovable" or "false." A provable statement with no free variables is a "theorem" of Σ.

In a sophisticated system, it may be that the provability or disprovability of a particular statement cannot be determined by any automatic procedure.†　Furthermore, in such a system, there may be statements, which would otherwise qualify as theorems, for which no proof or disproof is possible.‡　Fortunately, we are not going to concern ourselves with the problem of finding a proof (see § 2-1)—our concern will be limited to the problem of determining whether a given proof is valid or not. Having laid the groundwork in the preceding chapters, we are now ready to present a set of rules by which a mathematical proof may be tested for validity.

5-2 THE TURNSTILE

In order to make assertions about validity, we introduce the symbol ⊢, sometimes called the **turnstile**, and sometimes called the **yield symbol**. If

---

† A. Church, A Note on the Entscheidungsproblem, *Journal of Symbolic Logic*, vol. 1, 1936, pp. 40–41, 101–102.
‡ See, for example, E. Nagel and J. R. Newman, Goedel's Proof, in *The World of Mathematics* (New York: Simon and Schuster, 1956), pp. 1668–1695.

$A_1, A_2, \ldots, A_r,$ and P are statements, then the string

$$A_1, A_2, \ldots, A_r \vdash P$$

may be read as

The assumptions A_1 through A_r yield P

or as

P may be deduced from the assumptions A_1 through A_r

We have set ourselves the task of describing just what the above verbalizations mean, and, according to the promise in § 2-1, of doing it in such a way that a competent clerk can check whether or not a particular example lives up to the description.

We shall want to discuss the rules and related topics as we go along. In discussing the whys and wherefores of the rules, our arguments will be in terms of the applications of the logic, and therefore in terms of truth and meaning, or the quasi-truths and quasi-meanings of standard mathematical systems. Each statement of a rule will be displayed in indented typography to separate it from the discussion.

$A_1, A_2, \ldots, A_r \vdash P$ means that there is a sequence of statements $S_1, S_2, \ldots, S_s$ such that S_s is the statement P, and for each i, S_i satisfies one of the descriptions given below as **Rules**.

The sequences S_1 through S_s is called a **demonstration that $A_1, A_2, \ldots,$ $A_r \vdash P$**. Of course, a demonstration is not unique for a given P and a given set of assumptions, for there are many ways of proving a provable statement. The sequential aspect of the statements S_i is essential, for there are usually several statements in the demonstration that may not be asserted unless certain others have preceded them.

The A_i's are, in the main, just those assumptions which are needed in the demonstration, although no harm is done if extra, unneeded assumptions are listed. Any statement of a system may be used as an assumption, even a statement having free occurrences of a variable. An assertion $\vdash P$ will mean that no assumptions are used in the demonstration.

5-3 RULES OF ASSUMPTION AND TAUTOLOGY

One can easily appreciate the futility of trying to argue the probable truth of the theory of biological evolution with an opponent who insists that every word of Genesis is literally true. Unless you and your forensic adversary can agree on a set of permissible assumptions, your choice of weapons will have to be something other than the rules of logic. This illustrates the necessity for our first rule, the *Rule of Assumption*.

Assumption: S_i is one of the statements A_1 through A_r.

We justified our interest in truth-table tautologies by the fact that any meaningful statement with a tautological structure would automatically be a true statement, regardless of its content. This is the justification for the second rule, the *Rule of Tautology*.

Tautology: S_i is a truth-table tautology.

5-4 RULES OF INSTANCE AND EXAMPLE

In § 4-2 we pointed out the necessity of permitting the application of a theorem expressed in terms of a, b, and c to a triangle named pqr. The next rule covers this need. Let us give it a traditional setting. For a long, long time, logicians have been in agreement that since every man is mortal, it follows that if Socrates is a man, then Socrates is mortal. Purifying the quantifier "every man" we get

$$\forall x[x \text{ is a man} \Rightarrow x \text{ is mortal}] \Rightarrow$$
$$[\text{Socrates is a man} \Rightarrow \text{Socrates is mortal}]$$

If we represent the substatement within the left pair of brackets by $P(x)$, then we can represent the whole statement by

$$\forall x P(x) \Rightarrow P(\text{Socrates})$$

This last formulation illustrates a use of the *Rule of Instance*, which says, in effect, that if a generalized statement is true, then any particularized instance of it is true. A difficulty may arise from undiscriminating use of the rule. If a variable, say y, has two or more occurrences all free or all within the scope of the same y quantifier, then these occurrences are not independent of each other (see § 4-7). For example, we cannot assert

$$\forall x[\exists y[y + 1 \neq x]] \Rightarrow \exists y[y + 1 \neq y + 1]$$

since, in the real numbers, the antecedent is true and the consequent false. In the antecedent, x and y can stand for different numbers, but in the consequent, both occurrences of y must represent the same number. For this reason, we have to place a restriction on the $P(x)$—$P(\alpha)$ pair involved here.

The *Rule of Example* is closely related to the Rule of Instance, and the same problem, in reverse, can arise in its use. In § 4-2 it was pointed out that to disprove the assertion

$$\forall x[(x + 3)^2 = x^2 + 3^2]$$

it would be sufficient to prove

$$\exists x[(x + 3)^2 \neq x^2 + 3^2]$$

Our method is simple; we take any nonzero number, say 2, and show that $(2 + 3)^2 \neq 2^2 + 3^2$. Having done so for a single example, we feel justified in claiming the general existence statement. In other words, if $P(\alpha)$ is true, then $\exists x P(x)$ should also be true. However, we cannot assert

$$\forall y[y + 1 = y + 1] \Rightarrow \exists x \forall y[x = y + 1]$$

since, again, the antecedent is true and the consequence false in the real numbers. The same restriction on the $P(x)$—$P(\alpha)$ pair takes care of the difficulties with both rules.

> **Instance:** S_i has the form $\forall x P(x) \Rightarrow P(\alpha)$

> **Example:** S_i has the form $P(\alpha) \Rightarrow \exists x P(x)$.

> Each rule is subject to the restriction that no variable occurring free in the term α may become bound by the substitution of α for x in the $P(x)$—$P(\alpha)$ pair.

EXERCISES

1. Find your own example illustrating the necessity of the restriction of the Rule of Instance. See whether you automatically have an example of the necessity for the restriction on the Rule of Example.

2. Find a new illustration of the necessity for the restriction on the Rule of Example, and see whether you have also found one for the restriction on the Rule of Instance.

3. Use the statement "Every man is of woman born" to illustrate the need for the restriction on the Rule of Instance, first converting the statement to quantifier and predicate variable notation. Assume a universe of normal people, and use the following dictionary:

$M(x)$: x is or was a man
$B(x, y)$: x gave birth to y

5-5 RULES OF CHOICE AND GENERALIZATION. SPECIFIED VARIABLES

In § 4-7 we referred to going from a statement

There is an x such that $x < z$

to the statement

Let t be such a number.

The *Rule of Choice* is directed to this problem of validating $P(t)$ on the strength of $\exists x P(x)$. We note that the free variable t so introduced now has special properties—those asserted by the predicate P. The statement we would like to allow is

$$\exists x[x < z] \Rightarrow t < z$$

However, t would be a poor choice for the variable if we had already used it as a free variable and had asserted

$$z < t$$

for then the conditional above would have a true antecedent and a false consequent. It is clear that z itself is also barred from use, even if we have made no previous assertion about it. So we must choose a letter, say y, which has not become unduly specialized in any way, and which will not encroach upon other variables in the statement.

A free variable, y, can become associated with special properties in just two ways. First, if y occurs free in an assumption, something significant may have been assumed about whatever the variable represents. Hence our first restriction is that y cannot appear free in any assumption. Second, y may acquire special properties by occurring free in a previous statement of the demonstration, if that statement involved the removal of an existential quantifier. In the example used in the beginning of this section, it is not only the specified variable t that has acquired special properties in removing the existential quantifier, but also the z. Thus if we have made the statement

$$\exists x[x < z] \Rightarrow t < z$$

we are barred from stating

$$\exists x[x < t] \Rightarrow z < t$$

since, in the real numbers, both antecedents would be true for any z and any t, but one of the consequents must be false. (Remember that free occurrences of the same variable are not independent, even if they are in different statements of a given demonstration.) On the other hand, there would be no objection to

$$\exists x[x < w] \Rightarrow z < w$$

as the second statement, provided w had not become specialized. This illustrates the thinking behind the two parts of the second restriction on this pair of rules. As to why Generalization† is mentioned in the restriction, along with Choice, we shall only say that it is in there to prevent Choice from sneaking in through a back door. We leave the interpretation of that remark for an exercise. (See Exercise 1, § 5-9.)

The Rule of Generalization relates to the question, also raised in § 4-2, of the validity of a claim of generality for whatever has been deduced. Most of our theorems and postulates, when formally stated, start off with a string of universal quantifiers. When invoking such a statement in the course of a proof, we can remove these quantifiers with the aid of Instance in order to talk about a particular but nonspecific instance. But if we are demonstrating a new *theorem*, we need a way of putting the quantifiers on again!

What we are after is permission to make a statement of the form

$$P(y) \Rightarrow \forall x P(x)$$

† In discussion, we shall frequently refer to rules this way, omitting "the Rule of."

However, if y has special properties, such a statement may be impossible. If, for example, it is true that $y < 0$, we cannot be permitted to state

$$y < 0 \Rightarrow \forall x[x < 0]$$

One can see why the restrictions on Generalization might be the same as those on Choice.

For convenience in stating the rules, we now define an expression already used informally in the preceding discussion.

Definition

> In a pair of statements of the form $P(y)$—$\forall x P(x)$ or the form $\exists x P(x)$—$P(y)$, y will be referred to as the **specified variable**.

And now the rules.

> **Choice:** S_i has the form $\exists x P(x) \Rightarrow P(y)$.

> **Generalization:** S_i has the form $P(y) \Rightarrow \forall x P(x)$.

> Each rule is subject to the following restrictions:
>
> (1) y is not a variable occurring free in any A_j, and
> (2) (a) y is not a variable occurring free in any previous use of Choice or Generalization, or
>   (b) no variable specified in a previous use of Choice or Generalization occurs free in $P(y)$.

The specified variable in a use of either of these rules must satisfy (1) and, in addition, (2a) *or* (2b).

5-6 RULES OF REFLEXIVITY OF EQUALITY, EQUALITY SUBSTITUTION, AND BICONDITIONAL SUBSTITUTION

Two of the next three rules legitimize "reasons" that are familiar from high school geometry. The Rule of Reflexivity of Equality is often given as "Identity" in geometry texts.

> **Reflexivity of Equality:** S_i has the form $\alpha = \alpha$.

A word of warning here—the terms on each side should be *formally identical*. The Rule of Reflexivity of Equality may not be used to justify a statement like $x + y = y + x$. If k, l, and m are distinct collinear points in that order, then line $\overset{\leftrightarrow}{kl} = $ line $\overset{\leftrightarrow}{lm}$ not by virture of the identity of two pictures, but presumably as a deducible statement.

The *Rule of Equality Substitution* is what is meant by the jargon "Equals may be substituted for equals." In a $P(\alpha)$—$P(\beta)$ pair, if $\alpha = \beta$, then $P(\alpha)$ should have the same meaning as $P(\beta)$. Unfortunately, it isn't quite that simple. In real numbers, the statement

$$\forall x \exists y [y < x]$$

is true. However, if we have stated about some particular x and some particular y that $y = x + y^2$, to allow unrestricted substitution would produce the false statement

$$\forall x \exists y [x + y^2 < x]$$

On the other hand, if we have an equality which is true for all x and all y, we need not worry about a variable becoming associated with another occurrence of itself as a result of a substitution based on that equality. (This is what happened above.) Thus, since it is true that $\forall xy [y = x + y - x]$, we can substitute in the original statement to obtain the true statement

$$\forall x \exists y [x + y - x < x]$$

The rule therefore requires that the equality be preceded by enough universal quantifiers to make the substitution a safe one.

Equality Substitution: S_i has the form

$$\forall x_1 x_2 \cdots x_m [\alpha = \beta] \Rightarrow [P(\alpha) \Leftrightarrow P(\beta)]$$

with the restriction that the x_j's must include all variables that occur free in α or β, but become bound in the $P(z)$—$P(\alpha)$ or $P(z)$—$P(\beta)$ substitutions implied in the $P(\alpha)$—$P(\beta)$ notation.

The biconditional relation between statements is, in many ways, analogous to equality of terms. One of those ways is the substitutability of one statement for another which is biconditionally related to it. This is the import of the

Rule of Biconditional Substitution. As with Equality Substitution, the biconditional must be sufficiently generalized to avoid trouble from the binding of free variables.

Biconditional Substitution: S_i has the form

$$\forall x_1 x_2 \cdots x_m [R \Leftrightarrow S] \Rightarrow [P \Leftrightarrow Q]$$

where

(1) Q is formed from P by substituting S for some or all of the occurrences of R in the composition of P, including possible uses of R to construct terms of P,

and

(2) the x_j's must include all variables which are free in R or S but which are bound in P or Q wherever they are involved in substitution.

If we may assert $\forall x_1 x_2 \cdots x_m [R \Leftrightarrow S]$ and the x_i's include *all* the free variables in $R \Leftrightarrow S$, then this rule, in effect, says that if S is substituted for R in *any* statement P of which R is a component, then the new statement will have the same truth value as P. For this reason, in any context in which $\forall x_1 x_2 \cdots x_m [R \Leftrightarrow S]$ is a permissible statement, with no free variables, we shall say that R and S are **logically equivalent**. In particular, if any biconditional is a truth-table tautology, its left and right sides are logically equivalent, for, as we shall see, there is a demonstration that $\forall x_1 x_2 \cdots x_m [R \Leftrightarrow S]$ may be deduced without use of any assumptions (see § 7-6).

5-7 THE RULE OF DETACHMENT

Up to this point, all the rules have described statements, which, if they can be made at all, may be made as early in the demonstration as you like. They may be prohibited from appearing in a particular form *after* certain others, but none of them needs *preceding* ones. If this were the only kind of permissible statement, all demonstrations would be trivial. The heart and soul of deductive logic is the building up to later statements by way of earlier ones. One last rule will bring life to all the others. This *Rule of Detachment* (also called the **Rule of Modus Ponens**) is deceptively simple in its wording, considering how productive it is. To motivate it, we shall once more call up the ghost of the man who has died so many deaths for illustrative purposes. If we have been permitted to assert

Socrates is human

and also

> If Socrates is human, then Socrates is mortal

then we may assert, according to this rule,

> Socrates is mortal.

> **Detachment:** There are two statements preceding S_i in the demonstration, having the forms

$$P \quad \text{and} \quad P \Rightarrow S_i$$

It is not required that the statement P precede the statement $P \Rightarrow S_i$, but only that both statements precede S_i itself.

EXERCISE

Other than the desire to have at least one constructive "rule of inference," no general justification for accepting Detachment was given. Supply it, basing your argument on Table 1d.

5-8 PRESENTING A DEMONSTRATION

Having named and described each of the rules, we can restate the definition given in § 5-2.

> $A_1, A_2, \ldots, A_r \vdash P$ means that there is a sequence of statements $S_1, S_2, \ldots, S_s$, such that S_s is the statement P, and for each i, S_i satisfies one of the following rules: Assumption, Tautology, Instance, Example, Choice, Generalization, Reflexivity of Equality, Equality Substitution, Biconditional Substitution, and Detachment.

And now that you know what a demonstration is, we can tell you what a provable statement is.

Definition

P is a **provable** (or **true**) **statement** of the system Σ if and only if $A_1, A_2, \ldots,$ $A_r \vdash P$, and each A_j is a postulate or a definition of Σ. A provable statement having no free variables is a **theorem** of the system.

The ten rules named in the definition of a demonstration form the basis for the system of logic presented in this text. As you see, they are concocted largely in terms of permissible arrangements of symbols. The two ingredients that might give trouble to our zealous clerk are, first, the problem of determining what constitutes a term, and, second, the problem of determining when a variable is bound within a term. These problems can be settled with some formality within each particular mathematical system.

We arrange a demonstration with the sequence S_1 through S_s numbered and stated on the left, and with the justification for each S_i stated on the right. Each justification must name one of the ten rules. For convenience, we shall adopt the following self-explanatory abbreviations for use in the justification column: **As, Tau, Inst, Exam, Ch, Gen, Ref Eq, Eq Sub, Bi Sub,** and **Det.** For some rules, certain other information should be given. It will help our eagle-eyed clerk if, in a use of Instance or Example, we indicate what α substitution has been made with the variable. We shall do so thus:

$$\text{Inst } x \rightarrow a + 2$$

or $\text{Exam } a + r \rightarrow y$

In using Choice and Generalization, it is important to indicate which variable is specified, and which others occur free, for your own use in guarding against violating the restrictions in later application of these rules. Thus

$$\text{Ch } \textcircled{x}, y, t$$

will mean

Rule of Choice, with x specified, and with y and t also free

By its definition, the specified variable *always* occurs free.

In a use of Detachment, the pair of preceding statements which make the step possible will be indicated by giving their position in the sequence on the left, thus:

$$\text{Det } S_2, S_4$$

It should be noted that in applications of Instance, Example, Choice, and Generalization, there might be no difference between the antecedent and the consequent except the presence or absence of a quantifier, as you may see in steps 4 and 8 in Example 1 below. Review the relevant comments at the end of § 4-9.

5-9 THREE SAMPLE DEMONSTRATIONS

We shall start with a relatively easy demonstration for a warm-up. Although the variables need no interpretation for the demonstration, it will do no harm if you think of x and y as representing real numbers.

Example 1

$$\exists xy[xy = yx] \vdash \exists yx[xy = yx]$$

Statement	*Justification*
1. $\exists xy[xy = yx]$	As
2. $\exists xy[xy = yx] \Rightarrow \exists y[ty = yt]$	Ch$\textcircled{t}$
3. $\exists y[ty = yt]$	Det S_1, S_2
4. $\exists y[ty = yt] \Rightarrow ty = yt$	Ch$\textcircled{y}$, t
5. $ty = yt$	Det S_3, S_4
6. $ty = yt \Rightarrow \exists x[xy = yx]$	Exam $t \rightarrow x$
7. $\exists x[xy = yx]$	Det S_5, S_6
8. $\exists x[xy = yx] \Rightarrow \exists yx[xy = yx]$	Exam $y \rightarrow y$
9. $\exists yx[xy = yx]$	Det S_7, S_8

Since S_9 is precisely the statement found to the right of the turnstile, we have arrived at the end of the demonstration. At S_2, t was specified arbitrarily. S_4 illustrates that the specified variable does not *have* to be a new one.

Example 2

$$A_1: \quad \forall xyz[x > y \wedge y > z \Rightarrow x > z]$$
$$A_2: \quad \forall xy[x > y \Rightarrow x \neq y]$$
$$A_1, A_2 \vdash \forall x[x > 0 \Rightarrow 0 \not> x]$$

It is usually more convenient for reference if the assumptions are listed this way, instead of being strung out in front of the turnstile. In the following demonstration, the first statement, S_1, is part of S_2, and we have done the obvious thing to save space (and labor).

The demonstration will be a formal version of the following argument: According to A_1, if $x > 0$ and $0 > x$, we would get $x > x$, and so, by A_2, $x \neq x$. Since nothing is different from itself, we cannot have both $x > 0$ and $0 > x$. Therefore, if $x > 0$, it must be that $0 \not> x$.

We start with A_1 and proceed to remove the quantifiers in order to talk about 0 and a particular, but unspecified, x.

Statement	*Justification*
1. $\forall xyz[x > y \land y > z \Rightarrow x > z]$	As A_1
2. $S_1 \Rightarrow \forall yz[x > y \land y > z \Rightarrow x > z]$	Inst $x \rightarrow x$
3. $\forall yz[x > y \land y > z \Rightarrow x > z]$	Det S_1, S_2

We now need a zero where y appears.

4. $S_3 \Rightarrow \forall z[x > 0 \land 0 > z \Rightarrow x > z]$	Inst $y \rightarrow 0$
5. $\forall z[x > 0 \land 0 > z \Rightarrow x > z]$	Det S_3, S_4

In removing this last quantifier, we must remember that we are aiming for the statement $x > x$.

6. $S_5 \Rightarrow [x > 0 \land 0 > x \Rightarrow x > x]$	Inst $z \rightarrow x$
7. $x > 0 \land 0 > x \Rightarrow x > x$	Det S_5, S_6

Now we wish to show that this last statement leads to the highly undesirable result that $x \neq x$. We must use A_2.

8. $\forall xy[x > y \Rightarrow x \neq y]$	As A_2
9. $S_8 \Rightarrow \forall y[x > y \Rightarrow x \neq y]$	Inst $x \rightarrow x$
10. $\forall y[x > y \Rightarrow x \neq y]$	Det S_8, S_9
11. $S_{10} \Rightarrow [x > x \Rightarrow x \neq x]$	Inst $y \rightarrow x$
12. $x > x \Rightarrow x \neq x$	Det S_{10}, S_{11}

At this point, our industrious but, alas, nonlogical clerk interrupts to ask: What's wrong with $x \neq x$? We gently remind him that

13. $x = x$ $\parallel$ Ref Eq

Having put that down, are we now ready to assert $x > 0 \Rightarrow 0 \not> x$? If so, which of the ten rules furnish the justification for the step? In high school you might have written "steps 7, 12, and 13" as your "reason," since the desired statement clearly "follows logically" from those steps. In a more detailed argument, you might say, "By S_7, $x > 0$ and $0 > x$ only if $x > x$. But by S_{12}, this would imply that $x \neq x$. Since S_{13} asserts that $x = x$, we know that the statement $x > 0 \wedge 0 > x$ must be false. Hence, if its first substatement is true, the second one must be false—that is, $x > 0 \Rightarrow 0 \not> x$." This argument has a noncoincidental resemblance to the short method of testing for tautology. In fact, if that kind of informal argument is valid, there will be a tautology we can use at this point in the demonstration to produce the same result. It will have the form of a nested sequence of conditionals. We leave the testing of the tautology (S_{14}) to you.

14. $S_7 \Rightarrow S_{12} \Rightarrow S_{13} \Rightarrow [x > 0 \Rightarrow 0 \not> x]$ $\parallel$ Tau

A simple beheading process, repeated three times, cuts S_{14} down to the desired kernel.

15. $S_{12} \Rightarrow S_{13} \Rightarrow [x > 0 \Rightarrow 0 \not> x]$ $\parallel\parallel$ Det S_7, S_{14}

16. $S_{13} \Rightarrow [x > 0 \Rightarrow 0 \not> x]$ Det S_{12}, S_{15}

17. $x > 0 \Rightarrow 0 \not> x$ Det S_{13}, S_{16}

After a quick check of A_1, A_2, and the right-hand column for forbidden free variables, we proceed to restore the one quantifier needed.

18. $S_{17} \Rightarrow \forall x[x > 0 \Rightarrow 0 \not> x]$ $\parallel\parallel$ Gen $\circledx$

19. $\forall x[x > 0 \Rightarrow 0 \not> x]$ Det S_{17}, S_{18}

That was something of a workout. For a change of mood, let us go on to a geometric theorem.

Example 3

We take as axioms

     A_1:   For any two distinct points, there is a line connecting them.
     A_2:   There exist (at least) two distinct points.

Our theorem is

     Every point is on at least one line.

Informal proof: Let us call the points of A_2 z and y. Take any point x. Either it will be the same as z, and thus different from y, giving us a line connecting x and y, or it will be different from z, giving us a line through x and z. In either case x is on a line, and thus every point is on at least one line.

     Before giving the demonstration, we shall cast the axioms and the theorem in more convenient symbolic form, using the following dictionary.

         $P(x)$: x is a point
         $L(x)$: x is a line
         $C(x, y)$: x is on y

     Before you read the next few lines, try translating the axioms and the theorem, using the given dictionary.

*   *   *

     Even if they vary a little from the ones below, your formulas might still be correct. We shall use these:

     A_1: $\forall xy[P(x) \wedge P(y) \wedge x \neq y \Rightarrow \exists m[L(m) \wedge C(x, m) \wedge C(y, m)]]$
     A_2: $\exists xy[P(x) \wedge P(y) \wedge x \neq y]$
     $A_1, A_2 \vdash \forall x[P(x) \Rightarrow \exists m[L(m) \wedge C(x, m)]]$

Statement	*Justification*
1. $\exists xy[P(x) \wedge P(y) \wedge x \neq y]$	As A_2
2. $S_1 \Rightarrow \exists y[P(z) \wedge P(y) \wedge z \neq y]$	Ch $\textcircled{z}$
3. $\exists y[P(z) \wedge P(y) \wedge z \neq y]$	Det S_1, S_2
4. $S_3 \Rightarrow P(z) \wedge P(y) \wedge z \neq y$	Ch $\textcircled{y}$, z
5. $P(z) \wedge P(y) \wedge z \neq y$	Det S_3, S_4

These first five steps are the formal equivalent of "Let us call the points of A_2 z and y."

6. $x = z \Rightarrow [S_5 \Leftrightarrow P(x) \wedge P(y) \wedge x \neq y]$ $\parallel$ Eq Sub

It now appears "logical" that, between S_5 and S_6 we have enough to guarantee that if $x = z$, then $P(x) \wedge P(y) \wedge x \neq y$. On the other hand, if $x \neq z$, even though S_5 implies $P(z)$ tautologically we cannot deduce that $P(x) \wedge P(z) \wedge x \neq z$, for x might be a hippogryph instead of a point. Looking again at the theorem, we find that it will be enough if we can say "If $P(x)$, then ...." Moreover, since $x = z \vee x \neq z$ is tautological, we should be able to get $P(x) \Rightarrow [P(x) \wedge P(y) \wedge x \neq y] \vee [P(x) \wedge P(z) \wedge x \neq z]$. The relevant tautology is:

7. $S_5 \Rightarrow S_6 \Rightarrow [P(x) \Rightarrow [P(x) \wedge P(y) \wedge$

   $x \neq y] \vee [P(x) \wedge P(z) \wedge x \neq z]]$ $\parallel$ Tau

We now proceed to behead this statement.

8. $S_6 \Rightarrow [P(x) \Rightarrow [P(x) \wedge P(y) \wedge x \neq y]$

   $\vee [P(x) \wedge P(z) \wedge x \neq z]]$ $\parallel$ Det S_5, S_7

9. $P(x) \Rightarrow [P(x) \wedge P(y) \wedge x \neq y]$

   $\vee [P(x) \wedge P(z) \wedge x \neq z]$ $\parallel$ Det S_6, S_8

Now we need to show that each of the alternatives in the consequent of S_9 leads to the same result: $\exists m[L(m) \wedge C(x, m)]$. So we start with

10. $\forall xy[P(x) \wedge P(y) \wedge x \neq y$

    $\Rightarrow \exists m[L(m) \wedge C(x, m) \wedge C(y, m)]]$ $\parallel$ As A_1

11. $S_{10} \Rightarrow \forall y[P(x) \wedge P(y) \wedge x \neq y$

    $\Rightarrow \exists m[L(m) \wedge C(x, m) \wedge C(y, m)]]$ $\parallel$ Inst $x \to x$

12. $\forall y[P(x) \wedge P(y) \wedge x \neq y$

    $\Rightarrow \exists m[L(m) \wedge C(x, m) \wedge C(y, m)]]$ $\parallel$ Det S_{10}, S_{11}

13. $S_{12} \Rightarrow [P(x) \wedge P(y) \wedge x \neq y$

    $\Rightarrow \exists m[L(m) \wedge C(x, m) \wedge C(y, m)]]$ $\parallel$ Inst $y \to y$

14. $P(x) \wedge P(y) \wedge x \neq y$

    $\Rightarrow \exists m[L(m) \wedge C(x, m) \wedge C(y, m)]$ $\parallel$ Det S_{12}, S_{13}

This is more than we want; $C(y, m)$ is superfluous. We play around with the consequent of S_{14} for a couple of steps.

15. $\exists m[L(m) \wedge C(x, m) \wedge C(y, m)]$
     $\Rightarrow L(m) \wedge C(x, m) \wedge C(y, m)$ ‖ Ch $\textcircled{m}$, x, y

16. $L(m) \wedge C(x, m) \Rightarrow \exists m[L(m) \wedge C(x, m)]$ ‖ Exam $m \to m$

It may look as though we have skipped a necessary link in the chain here, namely, $L(m) \wedge C(x, m) \wedge C(y, m) \Rightarrow L(m) \wedge C(x, m)$. However, since that statement is tautological, we can safely omit it from the chain of conditionals in S_{17}. (It will do no harm if it is included.)

17. $S_{14} \Rightarrow S_{15} \Rightarrow S_{16} \Rightarrow [P(x) \wedge P(y) \wedge$
    $x \neq y \Rightarrow \exists m[L(m) \wedge C(x, m)]]$ ‖ Tau

Three uses of Detachment brings us to

20. $P(x) \wedge P(y) \wedge x \neq y$
            $\Rightarrow \exists m[L(m) \wedge C(x, m)]$ ‖ Det S_{16}, S_{19}

We now go back to S_{12} (not S_{10}!) to derive the corresponding statement for the other alternative in the consequent of S_9.

21. $S_{12} \Rightarrow [P(x) \wedge P(z) \wedge x \neq z$
      $\Rightarrow \exists m[L(m) \wedge C(x, m) \wedge C(z, m)]]$ ‖ Inst $y \to z$

22. $P(x) \wedge P(z) \wedge x \neq z$
      $\Rightarrow \exists m[L(m) \wedge C(x, m) \wedge C(z, m)]]$ ‖ Det S_{12}, S_{21}

23. $\exists m[L(m) \wedge C(x, m) \wedge C(z, m)]$
        $\Rightarrow L(n) \wedge C(x, n) \wedge C(z, n)$ ‖ Ch $\textcircled{n}$, z, x

(Must we specify a new variable here?)

24. $L(n) \wedge C(x, n) \Rightarrow \exists m[L(m) \wedge C(x, m)]$ ‖ Exam $n \to m$

Repeating the processes of S_{17} through S_{20}, we come to

28. $P(x) \wedge P(z) \wedge x \neq z$
            $\Rightarrow \exists m[L(m) \wedge C(x, m)]$ ‖ Det S_{23}, S_{27}

Now we gather up the parts.

29. $S_9 \Rightarrow S_{20} \Rightarrow S_{28}$
    $\Rightarrow [P(x) \Rightarrow \exists m[L(m) \wedge C(x, m)]]$ $\quad\Vert$ Tau

32. $P(x) \Rightarrow \exists m[L(m) \wedge C(x, m)]$ $\quad\Vert$ Det S_{28}, S_{31}

After checking that x is not a forbidden variable for generalization, we put on the quantifier.

33. $S_{32} \Rightarrow \forall x[P(x) \Rightarrow \exists m[L(m) \wedge C(x, m)]]$ $\quad\Vert$ Gen $\circledx$

34. $\forall x[P(x) \Rightarrow \exists m[L(m) \wedge C(x, m)]]$ $\quad\Vert$ Det S_{32}, S_{33}

If a demonstration of a trivial theorem can take over 30 steps, can you imagine how many steps would be neeeded for the demonstration of a complicated one? If only postulates and definitions were allowed as assumptions, the steps could number in the thousands! Clearly, no mathematician in his right mind is going to insist upon doing proofs this way.

What, then, does this chapter accomplish? Simply this—it exhibits a very short list of rules which are intuitively so acceptable that there should be some confidence in the validity of proofs that are based on them.

In succeeding chapters we shall develop a great many other rules, permitting many other kinds of steps, thus enabling you to present much shorter proofs, more like the ones that you are familiar with. We shall not stretch your faith in us any further by asking you to accept these new rules, also, on intuitive grounds. The line of attack will be to show that each new rule is only a convenience—that any proof using a new rule could be replaced by a demonstration which eschewed it. The ten rules of this chapter will remain as the basis of the system of logic, and, to the extent that you have confidence in them, our arguments should give you confidence in the enlarged set.

EXERCISES

1. **(a)** Suppose we have a $P(x)$—$P(y)$ pair meeting all the conditions for a use of Generalization, with y specified. Would $\sim P(x)$—$\sim P(y)$ also meet those conditions?

(b) If so, write down such a step, and show how, in two more steps, you can get

$$\sim \forall x \sim P(x) \Rightarrow P(y)$$

(c) Use the results of Exercise 11 of § 4-1 to simplify this formula. Have you found the "back door" for the Rule of Choice? (See § 5-5.)

(d) Do we really need ten rules? Are there any other rules which might be dispensed with?

2. Supply the missing steps immediately preceding S_{20} of Example 3.

3. Supply the missing steps immediately preceding S_{32} of Example 3.

4. Construct a demonstration that

$$\forall xy[x + y = y + x] \vdash \forall yx[x + y = y + x]$$

5. Construct a demonstration that

$$\exists x\forall y[x + y = y] \vdash \forall y\exists x[x + y = y]$$

6. (a) With the demonstration of Exercise 5 as a model, try to construct a demonstration that

$$\forall x\exists y[x > y] \vdash \exists y\forall x[x > y]$$

and point out how our rules prevent such a demonstration.

(b) Is this good or bad for the Logicians?

7. Show that $\exists x\forall y[x = y + 1]$ (see § 5-4) leads to trouble in the real numbers, by constructing a demonstration that

$$\exists x\forall y[x = y + 1] \vdash 1 + 1 = 2 + 1$$

(*Hint:* You must use Inst twice.)

In Exercise 16 of § 4-8 you were asked to express $\exists_1 xP(x)$, "There exists exactly one x such that $P(x)$," in terms of the usual quantifiers. One possible correct answer is

$$\exists x[P(x) \wedge \forall y[P(y) \Rightarrow x = y]]$$

Informally, this says, "There is something for which the predicate P holds, and anything for which P holds must be that something." A more elegant formula is

$$\exists x \forall y [P(y) \Leftrightarrow x = y]$$

Informally, this one says, "There is something such that asserting P is true of anything is equivalent to asserting that the latter is that something."

8. Construct a demonstration that $\exists_1 x P(x) \vdash \exists x P(x)$, using the first version of $\exists_1 x P(x)$ given above.

9. Construct a demonstration that $\exists_1 x P(x) \vdash \exists x P(x)$, using the second version given above.

We had worked out demonstrations that each of the versions of $\exists_1 x P(x)$ yields the other, but our clerk dropped them into a puddle on the way to the typist, and parts were obliterated. In the first demonstration, the right-hand column suffered most, and in the second one, which was on the back of the same page, the left-hand column got it. However, our brilliant, if clumsy, former clerk was able to reconstruct the missing parts. Can you?

10. Fill in the missing parts for a demonstration that

$$\exists x [P(x) \wedge \forall y [P(y) \Rightarrow x = y]] \vdash \exists x \forall y [P(y) \Leftrightarrow x = y]$$

Statement	*Justification*
1. $\exists x [P(x) \wedge \forall y [P(y) \Rightarrow x = y]]$	
2. $S_1 \Rightarrow P(x) \wedge \forall y [P(y) \Rightarrow x = y]$	
3. $P(x) \wedge \forall y [P(y) \Rightarrow x = y]$	
4. $S_3 \Rightarrow \forall y [P(y) \Rightarrow x = y]$	
5. $\forall y [P(y) \Rightarrow x = y]$	
6. $S_5 \Rightarrow [P(y) \Rightarrow x = y]$	
7. $P(y) \Rightarrow x = y$	
8. $x = y \Rightarrow [P(x) \Leftrightarrow P(y)]$	
9. $S_3 \Rightarrow S_7 \Rightarrow S_8 \Rightarrow [P(y) \Leftrightarrow x = y]$	

Steps S_{10} through S_{15} were a total loss.

16. $\exists x \forall y [P(y) \Leftrightarrow x = y]$ $\|$

11. The second demonstration gave him a little more trouble. He was stumped by S_6, until he found a clue in S_7. At S_{10} he made a natural error, but the justification for S_{11} set him straight. A little further on, he decided to begin at the end and work back. Fill in the missing parts for a demonstration that

$$\exists x \forall y [P(y) \Leftrightarrow x = y] \vdash \exists x [P(x) \wedge \forall y [P(y) \Rightarrow x = y]]$$

Statement	*Justification*
	1. As
	2. Ch $\circledast{x}$
	3. Det S_1, S_2
	4. Inst $y \rightarrow y$
	5. Det S_3, S_4
	6. Tau
7. $P(y) \Rightarrow x = y$	7. Det S_5, S_6
	8. Gen $\circledy$, x
	9. Det S_7, S_8
	10. Inst $y \rightarrow x$
	11. Det S_3, S_{10}
	12. Ref Eq
	13. Tau
	14. Det S_{11}, S_{13}
	15. Det S_{12}, S_{14}
	16. Det S_9, S_{15}
	17. Exam $x \rightarrow x$
	18. Det S_{16}, S_{17}

12. Give two plausible, but nonequivalent interpretations of $\exists_1 xyP(x, y)$. (We shall not use this form of quantifier with more than one variable.)

5-10 EQUIVALENCE RELATIONS

The main purpose of this section is to provide more practice with demonstrations, using a collection of statements pertaining to equivalence relations.

A *binary* relation is one that refers to pairs of objects of a system. If we let R represent a binary relation, we can form atomic statements by writing α R β, meaning "α has the relation R to β." We could use the two-place predicate notation $R(\alpha, \beta)$, but that notation is also used for statements that are not atomic, or which contain other terms besides those mentioned in $R(\alpha, \beta)$.

A binary relation in a set may have a variety of special properties. An important class of binary relations are those known as *equivalence relations.* (Equality is one of these, see § 8-4.) A relation R is an **equivalence relation in** S if and only if it satisfies the following three conditions for every x, y, z, in S:

    i. x R x (Reflexivity)
    ii. If x R y, then y R x (Symmetry)
    iii. If x R y and y R z, then x R z (Transitivity)

Examples are easy to find.

Set S	*Interpretation of x R y*
1. People	x had the same parents as y
2. Geometric figures	x is congruent to y
3. Geometric figures	x is similar to y
4. Containers	capacity of x equals capacity of y

The most significant outcome of possessing these three properties is that an equivalence relation partitions S into nonoverlapping subsets, called the **equivalence classes with respect to** R. Each subset consists of just those members of S which are in the relation R to each other. In example 1 above, each equivalence class consists of sets of full siblings (as distinguished from half-siblings); in example 3 each class represents a unique shape, such as the shape of a cube.

With a given equivalence relation R, each element of S belongs to exactly one equivalence class. We shall denote that class by $\langle x \rangle$, where x is any element in the class. Thus in Example 3, for a certain triangle t, $\langle t \rangle$ would represent the set of all triangles similar to t, including itself. We shall prove that for a given R and a given x, $\langle x \rangle$ is well defined, by proving the assertion made at the beginning of this paragraph.

There will be three permissible atomic forms; x R y, $x \in \langle y \rangle$, and equalities. We shall be dealing with the following statements:

P_1: $\forall x[x \text{ R } x]$
P_2: $\forall xy[x \text{ R } y \Rightarrow y \text{ R } x]$
P_3: $\forall xyz[x \text{ R } y \wedge y \text{ R } z \Rightarrow x \text{ R } z]$
P_4: $\forall x \exists y[x \text{ R } y]$
P_5: $\forall xy[x \in \langle y \rangle \Leftrightarrow x \text{ R } y]$
P_6: $\forall xy[\forall z[z \in \langle x \rangle \Leftrightarrow z \in \langle y \rangle] \Rightarrow \langle x \rangle = \langle y \rangle]$
P_7: $\forall x[x \in \langle x \rangle]$
P_8: $\forall xy[x \text{ R } y \Leftrightarrow y \text{ R } x]$
P_9: $\forall xy[\forall z[z \in \langle x \rangle \Leftrightarrow z \in \langle y \rangle] \Leftrightarrow \langle x \rangle = \langle y \rangle]$
P_{10}: $\forall xy[x \in \langle y \rangle \Rightarrow \langle x \rangle = \langle y \rangle]$
P_{11}: $\forall xy[x \in \langle y \rangle \Leftrightarrow \langle x \rangle = \langle y \rangle]$
P_{12}: $\forall xy[\exists z[z \in \langle x \rangle \wedge z \in \langle y \rangle] \Rightarrow \langle x \rangle = \langle y \rangle]$

The statements P_1, P_2, and P_3 are the properties i, ii, and iii of an equivalence relation; P_5 amounts to a formal definition of the set $\langle y \rangle$, and P_6 is derived from a fundamental property of sets (see § 11-6). The statement P_4, while in itself not logically equivalent to P_1, may be substituted for that statement in describing an equivalence relation (see Exercises 1 and 2). The statement P_7 ensures that x is in the equivalence class named for it. The statement P_8 is a stronger version of P_2, as P_9 is of P_6. The statement P_{10} is mainly a lemma for the stronger P_{11}, which, in turn, is a lemma for P_{12}. Finally, P_{12} is logically equivalent to stating that distinct equivalence classes are disjoint, so that $\langle x \rangle$ cannot mean two different things.

We may take the set $\{P_1, P_2, P_3, P_5, P_6\}$ for our postulates, or the set $\{P_2, P_3, P_4, P_5, P_6\}$, the remaining statements in each case being theorems.

EXERCISES

1. Supply the steps for a demonstration that $P_1 \vdash P_4$.

P_1: $\forall x[x \text{ R } x]$
P_4: $\forall x \exists y[x \text{ R } y]$

Statement	*Justification*
	1. As
	2. Inst $x \to x$
	3. Det S_1, S_2
	4. Exam $x \to y$
	5. Det S_3, S_4
	6. Gen ⓧ
	7. Det S_5, S_6

2. Supply the missing statements and justifications for a demonstration that $P_2, P_3, P_4 \vdash P_1$.

P_1: $\forall x[x \mathrel{R} x]$
P_2: $\forall xy[x \mathrel{R} y \Rightarrow y \mathrel{R} x]$
P_3: $\forall xyz[x \mathrel{R} y \wedge y \mathrel{R} z \Rightarrow x \mathrel{R} z]$
P_4: $\forall x \exists y[x \mathrel{R} y]$

Statement	*Justification*
1. $\forall x \exists y[x \mathrel{R} y]$	
3. $\exists y[x \mathrel{R} y]$	3. Det S_1, S_2
4. $S_3 \Rightarrow x \mathrel{R} y$	
	5. Det S_3, S_4
6. $\forall xy[x \mathrel{R} y \Rightarrow y \mathrel{R} x]$	6. As P_2
	7. Inst $x \to x$
	8. Det S_6, S_7
	9. Inst $y \to y$
10. $x \mathrel{R} y \Rightarrow y \mathrel{R} x$	10. Det S_8, S_9
11. $\forall xyz[x \mathrel{R} y \wedge y \mathrel{R} z \Rightarrow x \mathrel{R} z]$	
17. $x \mathrel{R} y \wedge y \mathrel{R} x \Rightarrow x \mathrel{R} x$	
18. $S_5 \Rightarrow S_{10} \Rightarrow S_{17} \Rightarrow x \mathrel{R} x$	
21. $x \mathrel{R} x$	

Complete in two more steps.

3. **(a)** Write out and test the tautology in S_{18} above.

   (b) Describe what you did before writing down S_{22}.

4. Supply the missing statements and justifications for a 13-step demonstration that $P_1, P_5 \vdash P_7$.

$$P_1: \quad \forall x[x \text{ R } x]$$
$$P_5: \quad \forall xy[x \in \langle y \rangle \Leftrightarrow x \text{ R } y]$$
$$P_7: \quad \forall x[x \in \langle x \rangle]$$

Statement	*Justification*
5. $x \in \langle x \rangle \Leftrightarrow x \text{ R } x$	
8. $x \text{ R } x$	
9. $S_5 \Rightarrow S_8 \Rightarrow x \in \langle x \rangle$	

5. Construct a demonstration that $P_6 \vdash P_9$ (15 steps). Outline of demonstration: Remove the overall quantifiers from the assumption. Equality Substitution will start you on the converse. Use Generalization on z and a tautology to obtain the biconditional statement, and conclude in the usual way.

6. Construct a demonstration that $P_2 \vdash P_8$ (16 steps). Use Instance twice, with $x \rightarrow s$ and $y \rightarrow t$. Then repeat this process, with $x \rightarrow t$ and $y \rightarrow s$.

7. Why do you have to change variables in the preceding demonstration?

8. Supply the missing statements and justifications for a 48-step demonstration that $P_2, P_3, P_5, P_6 \vdash P_{10}$.

$$P_2: \quad \forall xy[x \text{ R } y \Rightarrow y \text{ R } x]$$
$$P_3: \quad \forall xyz[x \text{ R } y \wedge y \text{ R } z \Rightarrow x \text{ R } z]$$
$$P_5: \quad \forall xy[x \in \langle y \rangle \Leftrightarrow x \text{ R } y]$$
$$P_6: \quad \forall xy[\forall z[z \in \langle x \rangle \Leftrightarrow z \in \langle y \rangle] \Rightarrow \langle x \rangle = \langle y \rangle]$$
$$P_{10}: \quad \forall xy[x \in \langle y \rangle \Rightarrow \langle x \rangle = \langle y \rangle]$$

Statement	*Justification*

7. $s R y \wedge y R x \Rightarrow s R x$

13. $s R x \wedge x R y \Rightarrow s R y$

18. $x R y \Rightarrow y R x$

19. $S_7 \Rightarrow S_{13} \Rightarrow S_{18} \Rightarrow$
$$[x R y \Rightarrow [s R x \Leftrightarrow s R y]]$$

22.   22. Det S_{18}, S_{21}

27. $s \in \langle x \rangle \Leftrightarrow s R x$

29. $s \in \langle y \rangle \Leftrightarrow s R y$

30. $s \in \langle x \rangle \Leftrightarrow s \in \langle y \rangle \Rightarrow$
$$\forall z [z \in \langle x \rangle \Leftrightarrow z \in \langle y \rangle]$$

35. $\forall z [z \in \langle x \rangle \Leftrightarrow z \in \langle y \rangle] \Rightarrow \langle x \rangle = \langle y \rangle$

36. $S_{22} \Rightarrow S_{27} \Rightarrow S_{29} \Rightarrow S_{30} \Rightarrow S_{35} \Rightarrow$
$$[x R y \Rightarrow \langle x \rangle = \langle y \rangle]$$

41. $x R y \Rightarrow \langle x \rangle = \langle y \rangle$

42. $S_{23} \Rightarrow [S_{41} \Leftrightarrow [x \in \langle y \rangle \Rightarrow \langle x \rangle = \langle y \rangle]]$

43. $S_{41} \Leftrightarrow [x \in \langle y \rangle \Rightarrow \langle x \rangle = \langle y \rangle]$

44. $S_{43} \Rightarrow [S_{41} \Rightarrow [x \in \langle y \rangle \Rightarrow \langle x \rangle = \langle y \rangle]]$

9. Construct a demonstration that P_7, $P_{10} \vdash P_{11}$.

10. Construct a demonstration that $P_{11} \vdash P_{12}$.

Chapter 6

TWO MAJOR THEOREMS

6-1 INTRODUCTION

This chapter centers around two theorems concerning our system of logic. Relative to any mathematical system to which these rules will be applied, they are **metatheorems**, that is, theorems about theorems. In proving the metatheorems, we are not obliged to use the rules that were created for the formal proof of mathematical theorems; in fact, to do so would involve a species of circularity. On the other hand, if we are going to legitimize falling back upon meaning and intuitive logic at this level, we *are* obliged to present proofs in the form of simple and, we hope, convincing arguments.

In these theorems we are given permission to substitute other sequences of statements for a regular demonstration of $A_1, A_2, \ldots, A_n \vdash P$. The value of the substitute lies entirely in its relative brevity as a proof—*no end product can be obtained from a substitute sequence that is not already obtainable by sticking to the original rules.* The particular burden of the theorems of this chapter is to convince the reader of that fact. We are in no way changing the meaning of $A_1, A_2, \ldots, A_n \vdash P$. Demonstrations that have been shortened by applying the results of this chapter, or those of Chapters 7 and 8, will be called **abbreviated demonstrations**.

6-2 THE LEMMA THEOREM

Among the more familiar "reasons" not included in the decalogue of Chapter 5 is the one that justifies the referring to, or the quoting of, a previously proved theorem. Our first metatheorem, the *Lemma Theorem*, is to that point. A **lemma**, as the word is used by mathematicians, is a subsidiary statement which is proved to help in proving another statement. Frequently the only importance of a lemma lies in its use in the second proof.

Lemma Theorem: If

$$A_1, A_2, \ldots, A_m \vdash P \tag{$\mathcal{D}_1$}$$

and

$$P, B_1, B_2, \ldots, B_n \vdash Q \tag{$\mathcal{D}_2$}$$

and if no variable specified in the first demonstration occurs free in any B_i, and no variable specified in the second demonstration occurs free in any A_i, then

$$A_1, A_2, \ldots, A_m, B_1, B_2, \ldots, B_n \vdash Q \tag{$\mathcal{D}_3$}$$

There are three assertions here about demonstrations. The first relates to the proof of the lemma P, the second to a proof of the statement Q, using the lemma as an assumption, and the third asserts the existence of a proof of Q that does not assume P. We shall refer to these three demonstrations as $\mathcal{D}_1$, $\mathcal{D}_2$, and $\mathcal{D}_3$, respectively. *The Lemma Theorem is not itself a lemma.* It is a metatheorem permitting the use of lemmas in mathematical proofs.

Proof: The basic idea of our argument will be that we can replace an occurrence of P as a step of $\mathcal{D}_2$ by the whole sequence $\mathcal{D}_1$, which, of course, ends in P. Unfortunately for such a simple hope, some variables may have been specified in $\mathcal{D}_1$ which were also specified in $\mathcal{D}_2$, and simply inserting the first sequence into the second would thereby create a violation of the restrictions on Generalization and Choice. To get around this difficulty, we first construct a demonstration $\mathcal{D}_{2'}$ by rearranging $\mathcal{D}_2$. We start by adding P at the head of $\mathcal{D}_2$, with Assumption for its justification. Then, since nothing is gained in a demonstration by having any statement appear more than once as a step in itself, we can strike out all other uses of P as a step of $\mathcal{D}_2$. It is clear that the $\mathcal{D}_2$ thus obtained will still be a demonstration that $P, B_1, B_2, \ldots, B_n \vdash Q$.

Second, we amend $\mathcal{D}_1$ so that it can be safely inserted in the place of P in $\mathcal{D}_{2'}$. The only things we have to worry about are variables that are specified in both $\mathcal{D}_1$ and $\mathcal{D}_{2'}$. Suppose x is such a variable. Then it cannot occur free in P, nor in any A_i, so it is not necessary to retain it as a free variable in amending $\mathcal{D}_1$. Let us examine the effect of changing all free occurrences of x in any step to some entirely new variable, not used elsewhere in either demonstration, say x'. We shall assume that the changes are being made step by step, so that when we are considering some S_i, the substitution has already been made in every preceding step in which x occurs free. We must distinguish several cases, depending upon which of the ten rules is involved. In the following discussion of each rule, P' will be the predicate or statement formed from P by substituting x' for every *free* occurrence of x. Similarly, α' and β' will be terms formed from α and β by such substitution. (If there are no free occurrences of x in P, then P' will be P itself, and similarly for α' and β'.)

1. **Assumption:** x cannot occur free in any step justified by Assumption.

2. **Tautology:** The validity of a step justified by Tautology depends only on the five sentential operators, and not on the inner structure of any atomic sentence involved. In the sentential formula representing a statement justified by this rule, if all occurrences of P are changed to P' by the substitution, the tautological nature of the formula would be unaffected.

3. **Instance and Example**

   (a) If the step involves a $P(x)$—$P(\alpha)$ pair, then $P(x)$—$P(\alpha')$ will still satisfy the restrictions on these rules, since there is no chance that the new variable x' will become bound by the substitution of α' for x in the formation of the latter pair. In steps using these two rules, the x in $P(x)$ is actually bound by a quantifier, and therefore would not be replaced. The resulting statement, $\forall x P(x) \Rightarrow P(\alpha')$, or $P(\alpha') \Rightarrow \exists x P(x)$, will have no free occurrences of x.

   (b) If the step involves a $P(y)$—$P(\alpha)$ pair, with x occurring free in $P(y)$ or in $P(\alpha)$, then $P'(y)$—$P'(\alpha')$ will still be an allowable pair for application of each of these rules.

4. **Generalization and Choice**

   (a) If x is specified in a use of either of these rules, then it will have satisfied the conditions with regard to previous steps, and therefore so will x' with regard to the amended previous steps.

   (b) If x merely appears free in a statement of the form $P(z) \Rightarrow \forall y P(y)$ or $\exists y P(y) \Rightarrow P(z)$, then $P'(z) \Rightarrow \forall y P'(y)$ and $\exists y P'(y) \Rightarrow P'(z)$ will also be allowable.

5. **Reflexivity of Equality:** $\alpha' = \alpha'$ also satisfies the Rule of Reflexivity of Equality.

6. **Equality Substitution:** There are three subcases for this rule:
   (a) x is not free in α or β. Then

$$\forall x_1 x_2 \cdots x_n [\alpha = \beta] \Rightarrow P'(\alpha) \Leftrightarrow P'(\beta)$$

is also an instance of Equality Substitution.

(b) x is free in α or β and is not one of the x_i's mentioned in using the rule. Then

$$\forall x_1 x_2 \cdots x_n [\alpha' = \beta'] \Rightarrow P'(\alpha') \Leftrightarrow P'(\beta')$$

is also an instance of Equality Substitution.

(c) x is free in α or β and is one of the x_i's mentioned in using the rule. The rule requires only that the collection $\{x_1, x_2, \ldots, x_n\}$ shall include all the variables that are free in α or β and become bound in the $P(z)$—$P(\alpha)$ or $P(x)$—$P(\beta)$ substitution. It may be that others have been listed there as well, so we have to split this subcase into two subsubcases.

(i) x is, say, x_1, but does not become bound in the $P(z)$—$P(\alpha)$, $P(z)$—$P(\beta)$ substitutions. Then we replace S_i with the following five-step sequence:

$i_1.$ $\forall x_1 x_2 \cdots x_n [\alpha = \beta] \Rightarrow \forall x_2 x_3 \cdots x_n [\alpha' = \beta']$

$i_2.$ $\forall x_2 x_3 \cdots x_n [\alpha' = \beta'] \Rightarrow [P'(\alpha') \Leftrightarrow P'(\beta')]$

A tautology, followed by two steps using Detachment, gives us, at the second step of Detachment,

$i_5.$ $\forall x_1 x_2 \cdots x_n [\alpha = \beta] \Rightarrow [P'(\alpha') \Leftrightarrow P'(\beta')]$

(We have left the supplying of missing steps and reasons as an exercise.)

(ii) x is x_1, and cannot be omitted from the collection $\{x_1, x_2, \ldots, x_n\}$. Then there are occurrences of x that are free in α or β and become bound by the substitutions involved in the $P(\alpha)$—$P(\beta)$ construction. There may also be free occurrences of x in $P(\alpha)$ or $P(\beta)$. Then

$$\forall x_1 x_2 \cdots x_n [\alpha = \beta] \Rightarrow P'(\alpha) \Leftrightarrow P'(\beta)$$

is also an instance of Equality Substitution.

In this last case, it would appear that several occurrences of one variable, x, in $P(\alpha) \Leftrightarrow P(\beta)$ could turn into occurrences of two distinct variables in $P'(\alpha) \Leftrightarrow P'(\beta)$. However, bound and free occurrences of the same variable, or separately bound occurrences, are independent of each other, even in the same statement. For example, $\forall y[y^2 \geq 0] \Rightarrow x > 0$ is equivalent in meaning to $\forall x[x^2 \geq 0] \Rightarrow x > 0$. We can, in fact, formally prove their logical equivalence.

7. **Biconditional Substitution:** The argument for Equality Substitution can be copied for Biconditional Substitution.

8. **Detachment:** If S_i is justified by Detachment, then there were previous steps of the form P, $P \Rightarrow S_i$. These have presumably been changed to P', $P' \Rightarrow S_i'$. We can therefore justify S_i' by Detachment.

With the establishing of this theorem, a new kind of step can be permitted in a demonstration. We can put down the exact statement of a previously proved lemma or theorem as a step, provided it meets the restrictions given above, using an identifying reference (such as a theorem number) as its justification.

EXERCISE

Supply all missing steps and reasons for the five-step sequence in case 6c(i) above.

6-3 THE GENERAL DEDUCTION THEOREM

Another reason found in high school geometry proofs, but not covered in Chapter 5, is the one usually indicated by "Hypothesis" or "Given." Recall how you would prove the theorem:

     If two sides of a triangle are congruent, then the angles opposite them are congruent.

Given: $\overline{ab} \simeq \overline{ac}$

To prove: $\sphericalangle abc \simeq \sphericalangle acb$

You were permitted to assume that two sides, say $\overline{ab}$ and $\overline{ac}$, were in fact congruent. You were then allowed to use this statement to deduce, if you were able, the conclusion, $\sphericalangle abc \simeq \sphericalangle acb$.

Similar procedures are found in a proof "by cases." In a proof that there is no greatest prime number, we are concerned with nonnegative integers. We take any number n, and consider the number $m = n! + 1$. We then show:

1. If m is prime, then it is a prime number greater than n.

2. If m is not prime, then it has a prime factor greater than n.

Thus, since either m is prime or m is not prime, there is always a prime number greater than any given number n.

This is a fairly typical proof by cases. If we can show that each substatement of a disjunction ("m is prime or m is not prime") leads to the same conclusion ("There is a prime number greater than n"), then we can assert that the disjunction implies the conclusion. In our proof, we use the substatements of the disjunction as temporary assumptions in order to get certain conditional statements. From the conditionals $P \Rightarrow C$ and $Q \Rightarrow C$, the statement $P \lor Q \Rightarrow C$ follows tautologically. If, as in the above example, $P \lor Q$ can also be asserted, then we may assert C. The big question here is the propriety of assuming P in the course of establishing $P \Rightarrow C$. The next theorem legitimizes such temporary assumptions.

> **Deduction Theorem:** Let $\mathfrak{D}_2$: $S_1, S_2, \ldots, S_m \,(= H), S_{m+1}, \ldots,$
> $S_s \,(= C)$ be a sequence of statements such that:
> (a) $\mathfrak{D}_1$: $S_1, S_2, \ldots, S_{m-1}$ is a demonstration that $A_1, A_2, \ldots,$
> $A_n \vdash S_{m-1}$, and
> (b) $\mathfrak{D}_2$ satisfies the rules of a demonstration that $A_1, A_2, \ldots, A_n,$
> $H \vdash C$ except that for the use of Choice or Generalization in
>   any S_i with $i < m$, the presence of free variables in H shall
>   not be a restriction.
> We assume further that S_m is the only use of H as a step of $\mathfrak{D}_2$
> Then there is a demonstration, $\mathfrak{D}_3$, that $A_1, A_2, \ldots, A_n \vdash H \Rightarrow C$.

Proof: Our proof will consist in showing how the sequence $\mathfrak{D}_2$ can be replaced with a (longer) sequence $\mathfrak{D}_3$ in such a way that, for each S_i in $\mathfrak{D}_2$, the sequence $\mathfrak{D}_3$ will contain a statement $H \Rightarrow S_i$. In particular, the last statement of $\mathfrak{D}_3$ will be $H \Rightarrow C$. If H appears at all as a step, it will not be justified by Assumption, and so can be dropped from the assumptions for $\mathfrak{D}_3$. Again we must distinguish different cases.

1. Suppose S_i is not H, and was justified in $\mathfrak{D}_2$ by any rule except Detachment. Then the following sequence of three steps in $\mathfrak{D}_3$ replaces that step in $\mathfrak{D}_2$.

Statement	*Justification*
$i_1.$ S_i	Same rule as in $\mathfrak{D}_2$
$i_2.$ $S_i \Rightarrow [H \Rightarrow S_i]$	Tau
$i_3.$ $H \Rightarrow S_i$	Det

The first of these steps will be legal in $\mathfrak{D}_3$, since removing H as an allowable assumption introduces no additional restriction against any step of $\mathfrak{D}_2$ that fits the description of this S_i.

2. Suppose S_i is H (that is, $i = m$). Then we replace it with the tautology $H \Rightarrow H$.

3. Finally, suppose S_i was justified by Detachment. Then there were earlier steps P and $P \Rightarrow S_i$. By the time we get to S_i in a program of successive replacement, there will have been steps constructed for $\mathfrak{D}_3$ with the forms $H \Rightarrow P$ and $H \Rightarrow [P \Rightarrow S_i]$. We replace S_i with the following sequence.

Statement	*Justification*
$i_1.$ $[H \Rightarrow P] \Rightarrow [H \Rightarrow [P \Rightarrow S_i]] \Rightarrow [H \Rightarrow S_i]$	Tau
$i_2.$ $[H \Rightarrow [P \Rightarrow S_i]] \Rightarrow [H \Rightarrow S_i]$	Det
$i_3.$ $H \Rightarrow S_i$	Det

This theorem permits us to proceed with a demonstration as though H were not one of our assumptions (steps S_1 through S_{m-1}) until we actually need it, provided we are only aiming at $H \Rightarrow C$. However, the statements S_m to S_s cannot be claimed to have been deduced from the A_i assumptions, because those steps might have depended on the assumption of H. Therefore, they are restricted insofar as any use of Choice or Generalization is concerned, by the possible presence of free variables in H.

In applying the Deduction Theorem, $H \Rightarrow C$ will not usually be the final statement at which we are aiming. Let us consider the following theorem concerning integers:

(1) If n is odd, then n^2 has a remainder of 1 when divided by 8.

A natural way to start the proof of this theorem is:

(2) Let n be any odd integer. Then $n = 2k + 1$ for some integer k.

We then proceed to show that $n^2 = 8m + 1$ for some integer m.

Let us express the theorem formally, with variables restricted to integers.

(3) $\forall n [\exists k [n = 2k + 1] \Rightarrow \exists m [n^2 = 8m + 1]]$

Statement (2) is approximated in a formal procedure by assuming

(4) $\exists k\,[n = 2k + 1]$

and using Choice to remove the quantifier. By the Deduction Theorem, it is allowable to make that assumption, if we are proving

(5) $\exists k\,[n = 2k + 1] \Rightarrow \exists m\,[n^2 = 8m + 1]$

but we are out to prove something more. We still need to use Generalization to get statement (3), and the variable that we would have to specify, n, occurs free in the assumed statement (4). Are we not in trouble?

What the Deduction Theorem proves for this case is that there actually is a demonstration of which the last step is (5), and in which (4) is *not* an assumption. We can therefore continue as though we were actually producing that other demonstration, and so use Generalization without worrying about the free variable in (4).

On the other hand, there is danger in a later use of any S_i as a "previous statement," if $m \le i \le s$, since that S_i may have required the assumption of H. The simplest way to be safe is to give up the right to so use any such S_i, unless it can be established outside the S_m through S_s subsequence. The statement $H \Rightarrow S_i$ remains assertable for any S_i of that subsequence.

It is a good idea to use some device, such as an extended bracket, to the left of the statements S_m through S_s in the demonstration, to guard against improper later use of these steps. The step S_m (H), will have "Temporary Assumption," or "Temp As," for short, as its justification. Having arrived at S_s (C), we can go on with S_{s+1} $(H \Rightarrow C)$ using "Deduction Theorem" or "Ded Th" as the justification for that statement.

The resulting sequence, $\mathfrak{D}_3$, will usually be far from the most economical one possible for $A_1, A_2, \ldots, A_n \vdash H \Rightarrow C$. For example, if S_i in $\mathfrak{D}_2$ has been justified by Tautology, $H \Rightarrow S_i$ can also be justified (in $\mathfrak{D}_3$) by Tautology, and so the three-step sequence is not really needed. Consideration of points like this only complicates the proof of the Deduction Theorem without adding to that theorem's power.

6-4 THREE COROLLARIES

We leave the proof of the following three metatheorems to the student.

> **Deduction Theorem Corollary:** If $A_1, A_2, \ldots, A_n, H \vdash C$, then $A_1, A_2, \ldots, A_n \vdash H \Rightarrow C$.

We may use "Deduction Theorem" to refer to this theorem also.

Conjunction Theorem: If

$$A_1, A_2, \ldots, A_n \vdash P \qquad (\mathcal{D}_1)$$

and

$$B_1, B_2, \ldots, B_m \vdash Q \qquad (\mathcal{D}_2)$$

and if no variable specified in $\mathcal{D}_1$ occurs free in any B_i, and no variable specified in $\mathcal{D}_2$ occurs free in P or in any A_i, then

$$A_1, A_2, \ldots, A_n, B_1, B_2, \ldots, B_m \vdash P \wedge Q$$

Biconditional Theorem: If

$$A_1, A_2, \ldots, A_n, P \vdash Q$$

and

$$B_1, B_2, \ldots, B_m, Q \vdash P$$

and if no variable specified in $\mathcal{D}_1$ occurs free in any B_i, and no variable specified in $\mathcal{D}_2$ occurs free in P or in any A_i, then

$$A_1, A_2, \ldots, A_n, B_1, B_2, \ldots, B_m \vdash P \Leftrightarrow Q$$

These theorems would be invoked in the following way. If, for instance, we were to use the Conjunction Theorem, we would produce (or prove the existence of) $\mathcal{D}_1$ and $\mathcal{D}_2$. Having done so, we conclude by saying, "Hence by the Conjunction Theorem, $A_1, A_2, \ldots, A_n, B_1, B_2, \ldots, B_m \vdash P \wedge Q$."

EXERCISES

1. Prove the Deduction Theorem Corollary. (*Hint:* Show that the demonstration whose existence is assumed can be considered as an instance of the second demonstration, with temporary assumptions.)

2. Prove the following metatheorem: If

$$A_1, A_2, \ldots, A_n, H, K \vdash C$$

then $A_1, A_2, \ldots, A_n \vdash H \wedge K \Rightarrow C$

(*Hint:* First show that $A_1, A_2, \ldots, A_n \vdash H \Rightarrow K \Rightarrow C$. Then show how you could continue, in order to obtain the desired statement.)

3. We can apply the Deduction Theorem to Example 1 of § 5-9 to prove that
   $\vdash \exists xy[xy = yx] \Rightarrow \exists yx[xy = yx]$. That is, the conditional statement can
   be demonstrated without any assumptions.
   (a) Show that the $\mathcal{D}_3$ prescribed by the construction used in the proof of
   the Deduction Theorem would have 25 steps, and write out the first 7 of
   these.
   (b) Can you find a shorter demonstration for this? It can be done in
   9 steps.

4. Prove the Conjunction Theorem. (*Suggestion:* First prove that there is a
   demonstration that $B_1, B_2, \ldots, B_n, P \vdash P \wedge Q$. Then use the Lemma
   Theorem. Show why the restrictions on free variables in the statement of
   the Conjunction Theorem are needed.)

5. Prove the Biconditional Theorem.

6. Both the Conjunction Theorem and the Biconditional Theorem are
   symmetrically stated insofar as P and Q are concerned, except in the
   free variable restrictions. Consider this fact and tell what it suggests to
   you.

7. Let B represent the conjunction of all the postulates and basic definitions
   of a mathematical system Σ.
   (a) Show that if T is any theorem of Σ, then $\vdash B \Rightarrow T$.
   (b) Since, in this sense, we can prove any theorem of any system without
   using any assumptions, what becomes of the distinction between two
   mathematical systems, for example, Euclidean geometry and number
   theory? Is there any?

Chapter 7

SUPPLEMENTARY INFERENCE

RULES

7-1 THE INFERENCE RULE SYMBOL

Like Chapter 6, this chapter deals with substitute sequences, but on an individual step basis. We are going to show that one may safely permit a large number of additions to the, so far, very short list of inference rules. We shall be even less formal here than in the last chapter, for each additional rule is so easily derived from the basis that it usually would be sufficient to describe the rule. For form's sake, in § 7-3 we shall state one theorem and give its proof in some detail, to establish the pattern of proof for the meta-theorems of this chapter.

There is a widely used abbreviation of the statement of an inference rule. It consists of a horizontal line, above which are placed the symbols representing the required "previous statements," separated by commas, below which is the symbol for the inferable statement. For instance, our one and only inference rule up to now, the Rule of Detachment, could be indicated by

$$\frac{P, P \Rightarrow S_i}{S_i}$$

or even by

$$\frac{P, P \Rightarrow Q}{Q}$$

The fact that P and $P \Rightarrow Q$ appear above the line is enough to tell us that they represent statements which must occur earlier in the sequence than Q. The order in which they appear above the line has no significance whatsoever.

There may be any number of formulas above the line, but what appears below the line must represent a single statement. Any restrictions, other than the ordering imposed by the line, must be separately and explicitly given.

7-2 THE PATTERN OF PROOF FOR NEW INFERENCE RULES

Suppose we want to add the rule called "Modus Tollens":

$$\frac{P \Rightarrow Q, \sim Q}{\sim P}$$

After defining Modus Tollens formally, as we did with the Rule of Detachment, the appropriate metatheorem would read:

> Let $\mathfrak{D}_1$: $S_1, S_2, \ldots, S_s$ be a sequence of statements obeying the rules of a demonstration that $A_1, A_2, \ldots, A_n \vdash S_s$, except that Modus Tollens is also admitted as a justification for a step. Then there is a demonstration $\mathfrak{D}_2$ that $A_1, A_2, \ldots, \vdash S_s$.

We shall abbreviate the foregoing statement by:

$$\text{The rule } \frac{P \Rightarrow Q, \sim Q}{\sim P} \text{ is admissible.}$$

The proof of this theorem is simple, and typical. We use the same method that was exploited in the proof of the Deduction Theorem, showing how we can substitute a sequence of steps that do not use the new rule for the step that does.

Proof: Let S_i be any step in $\mathfrak{D}_1$ that was justified by Modus Tollens. Then S_i is $\sim P$, and there are previous statements S_j: $P \Rightarrow Q$ and S_k: $\sim Q$. We can replace S_i by the following sequence:

i_1.	$[P \Rightarrow Q] \Rightarrow \sim Q \Rightarrow \sim P$	Tau
i_2.	$\sim Q \Rightarrow \sim P$	Det S_j, S_{i_1}
i_3.	$\sim P$	Det S_k, S_{i_2}

7-3 INFERENCE RULE FORMS OF THE RULES OF INSTANCE, EXAMPLE, CHOICE, GENERALIZATION, EQUALITY SUBSTITUTION, AND BICONDITIONAL SUBSTITUTION

In the examples of Chapter 5 you were undoubtedly impressed with the tedium of the task of removing a string of universal quantifiers. For instance, in Example 2 of § 5-13, 10 steps out of a total of 19 were used for just that purpose (and 2 more for putting one quantifier back on). We can halve the number of steps in this process just by combining the Rules of Instance and Detachment.

Subject to the restrictions of the Rule of Instance,

$$\text{the rule } \frac{\forall x P(x)}{P(\alpha)} \text{ is admissible.}$$

Proof: If S_i was a step justified by the above inference rule, then S_i is $P(\alpha)$, and there was a previous step S_j: $\forall x P(x)$. Replace S_i by:

$i_1.$	$\forall x P(x) \Rightarrow P(\alpha)$	Inst
$i_2.$	$P(\alpha)$	Det S_j, S_{i_1}

Since S_i was obtained without using the new rule, the new rule is admissible.

Similar inference rules may be derived without trouble from the others named in the title of this section. We shall refer to each of these inference rules by the same name as the rule from which it is derived with the help of Detachment. Naturally, any restriction on the original rule applies equally to the inference rule version.

EXERCISES

1. State and prove the inference rule form of Choice.

2. State and prove the inference rule form of Generalization.

3. State the inference rule forms of Example, Equality Substitution, and Biconditional Substitution.

4. Prove: With the same restrictions as in Equality Substitution,

$$\text{the rule } \frac{\forall x_1 x_2 \cdots x_m [\alpha = \beta], P(\alpha)}{P(\beta)} \text{ is admissible.}$$

5. Prove: With the same restrictions as in Biconditional Substitution,

$$\text{the rule } \frac{\forall x_1 x_2 \cdots x_m [R \Leftrightarrow S], P}{Q} \text{ is admissible.}$$

We shall refer to these rules, also, by the name of the rule from which they are derived.

Prove the admissibility of the following rules.

6. $\dfrac{\forall x P(x), \forall x Q(x)}{\exists x [P(x) \wedge Q(x)]}$

7. $\dfrac{\exists x [P(x) \wedge Q(x)]}{\exists x P(x)}$

8. $\dfrac{\exists x P(x)}{\exists x [P(x) \vee Q(x)]}$

9. $\dfrac{\exists x P(x), \forall x [P(x) \Rightarrow Q(x)]}{\exists x Q(x)}$

7-4 ITERATED USE OF THE RULES OF INSTANCE AND EXAMPLE

Even with the inference form of Instance admitted, you might become impatient with the necessity of writing out the four steps necessary to remove the quantifiers from

$$\forall xyzt [[x = y] \wedge [z = t] \Rightarrow x + z = y + t]$$

especially if you had to repeat the process a few times. Can we not make all four steps at once?

Not only can we do so, but in so doing we may avoid some trouble that can arise out of successive substitution. Suppose the unquantified statement we are aiming at is

$$[x + y = y + z] \wedge [t = t] \Rightarrow (x + y) + t = (y + z) + t$$

We are stopped at the very start, for we cannot use Instance, $x \to x + y$, without violating the restriction on that rule. We could decide to work with a different set of variables entirely, but the next theorem gives us a better way out, for we can extend Instance and Example to allow multiple application. To that end, we first extend the $P(x)$—$P(\alpha)$ notation in a natural way, as follows:

> $P(x_1, \ldots, x_n)$—$P(\alpha_1, \ldots, \alpha_n)$ will represent a pair of statements such that:
> (a) If $i \neq j$, then x_i and x_j are distinct variables
> (b) For each i, α_i is a term. If any x_i represents an element of a restricted class by notational convention, then α_i must represent an element of that class.
> (c) $P(\alpha_1, \ldots, \alpha_n)$ can be obtained from $P(x_1, \ldots, x_n)$ by substituting α_i for each free occurrence of x_i in $P(x_1, \ldots, x_n)$

The extended versions of the Rules of Instance and Example can now be written:

> The rules
>
> $$\frac{\forall x_1 x_2 \cdots x_n P(x_1, \ldots, x_n)}{P(\alpha_1, \ldots, \alpha_n)}$$

and

> $$\frac{P(\alpha_1, \ldots, \alpha_n)}{\exists x_1 x_2 \cdots x_n P(x_1, \ldots, x_n)}$$
>
> are admissible, provided that no variable occurring free in any α_i is bound in $P(\alpha_1, \ldots, \alpha_n)$, where α_i has replaced x_i.

Notice that the restriction needs only to be checked in the final statement, not in what would be the intermediate ones under the one-at-a-time rule. *The extended Rule of Instance may be used only to remove a sequence of overall universal quantifiers; the extended Rule of Example only to adjoin a sequence of overall existential quantifiers.* We cannot play this game with Generalization or Choice, since each use of these rules must be checked for forbidden specified variables.

We shall illustrate the nature of a proof of the admissibility of these extended rules by proving it for the Rule of Instance, with just three variables. For proper generalization to n variables, one would use the Finite Induction Principle.

Suppose, then, that S_i is $P(\alpha_1, \alpha_2, \alpha_3)$ and that S_i was justified on the basis of the extended rule and a previous statement S_k: $\forall xyzP(x, y, z)$. We choose three new variables, not needed elsewhere in the demonstration, say x', y', and z'. We now replace S_i by the following sequence (the justifications are obvious):

i_1. $\forall xyzP(x, y, z) \Rightarrow \forall yzP(x', y, z)$

i_2. $\forall yzP(x',y, z) \Rightarrow \forall zP(x', y', z)$

i_3. $\forall zP(x', y', z) \Rightarrow P(x', y', z')$

i_4. $P(x', y', z') \Rightarrow \forall z'P(x', y', z')$

i_5. $\forall z'P(x', y', z') \Rightarrow \forall y'z'P(x', y', z')$

i_6. $\forall y'z'P(x', y', z') \Rightarrow \forall x'y'z'P(x', y', z')$

i_7. $\forall x'y'z'P(x', y', z') \Rightarrow \forall y'z'P(\alpha_1, y', z')$

i_8. $\forall y'z'P(\alpha_1, y', z') \Rightarrow \forall z'P(\alpha_1, \alpha_2, z')$

i_9. $\forall z'P(\alpha_1, \alpha_2, z') \Rightarrow P(\alpha_1, \alpha_2, \alpha_3)$

We can now form a long tautological string of conditionals,

i_{10}. $S_1 \Rightarrow S_2 \Rightarrow \cdots \Rightarrow S_9 \Rightarrow S_k \Rightarrow P(\alpha_1, \alpha_2, \alpha_3)$

After ten applications of Detachment, we end up with

i_{20}. $P(\alpha_1, \alpha_2, \alpha_3)$

Since S_i was obtained without use of the new rule, the new rule is admissible.

In using any of the rules of this section, the practice of noting which previous step is involved, as already established for Detachment, should be followed. (This can be omitted if the "previous step" is the immediately preceding one.) We shall not use special names in referring to these rules in an abbreviated demonstration. Thus a justification for a use of extended instance might look like this:

$$\text{Inst } S_6 \, x \to x, \qquad y \to x, \qquad z \to x + y$$

EXERCISE

In the above proof, why is it necessary to choose new variables "not needed elsewhere in the demonstration"? How would you determine whether or not a variable was needed elsewhere?

7-5 THE TAUTOLOGICAL INFERENCE FAMILY

Modus Tollens is an example of a whole class of inference rules directly derivable from tautological conditionals. The words "large number" in the introductory paragraph of this chapter could at this point be changed to read "unlimited number." Many of them are of sufficiently frequent use to have earned names, like Modus Tollens. Characteristically, no variable, and so no quantifier, is involved in them. We list a few of the more useful ones below.

Inference rules with one statement above the line:

(1) $\dfrac{P}{P \vee Q}$ (2) $\dfrac{P}{Q \Rightarrow P}$ (3) $\dfrac{\sim P}{P \Rightarrow Q}$

(4) $\dfrac{P \wedge Q}{P}$ (5) $\dfrac{P \Rightarrow Q}{\sim Q \Rightarrow \sim P}$ (6) $\dfrac{P \Rightarrow Q \wedge \sim Q}{\sim P}$

(7) $\dfrac{Q \vee \sim Q \Rightarrow P}{P}$ (8) $\dfrac{P \wedge Q \Rightarrow R}{P \Rightarrow Q \Rightarrow R}$ (9) $\dfrac{P \Rightarrow Q \Rightarrow R}{P \wedge Q \Rightarrow R}$

Inference rules with two statements above the line:

$$(10) \quad \frac{P \Rightarrow Q, \sim Q}{\sim P} \qquad\qquad (11) \quad \frac{P, Q}{P \wedge Q} \qquad\qquad (12) \quad \frac{P, P \Leftrightarrow Q}{Q}$$

$$(13) \quad \frac{P \vee Q, \sim Q}{P} \qquad\qquad\qquad (14) \quad \frac{P \Rightarrow Q, P \Rightarrow \sim Q}{\sim P}$$

$$(15) \quad \frac{P \Rightarrow Q, \sim P \Rightarrow Q}{Q} \qquad\qquad (16) \quad \frac{P \Rightarrow Q, Q \Rightarrow R}{P \Rightarrow R}$$

$$(17) \quad \frac{P \Rightarrow Q, P \Rightarrow R}{P \Rightarrow Q \wedge R} \qquad\qquad (18) \quad \frac{P \Rightarrow Q, R \Rightarrow Q}{P \vee R \Rightarrow Q}$$

Inference rules with three statements above the line:

$$(19) \quad \frac{P, P \Rightarrow Q, Q \Rightarrow R}{R} \qquad\qquad (20) \quad \frac{P \Rightarrow Q, Q \Rightarrow R, \sim R}{\sim P}$$

$$(21) \quad \frac{P \Rightarrow Q, Q \Rightarrow R, R \Rightarrow P}{P \Leftrightarrow Q}$$

Several of these have obvious extensions. For example, (8) can be extended to

$$\frac{P_1 \wedge P_2 \wedge \cdots \wedge P_n \Rightarrow Q}{P_1 \Rightarrow P_2 \Rightarrow \cdots \Rightarrow P_n \Rightarrow Q}$$

Do not memorize this list. Look it over carefully, noting what the rules say, and in that way get an idea of what is possible.

In the form that we shall give it, this combination of Tautology and Detachment is a powerful step-saver. We are going to legitimize a kind of justification much like the "steps 7, 12, and 13" mentioned in discussing Example 2 of § 5-9. You may remember that a tautology and three uses of Detachment turned the trick. If the intuition was accurate, then the tautology was automatically determined:

$$S_7 \Rightarrow S_{12} \Rightarrow S_{13} \Rightarrow [x > 0 \Rightarrow 0 \not> x]$$

This is precisely the structure of Tautological Inference. Rule (18) is admissible because $[P \Rightarrow Q] \Rightarrow [R \Rightarrow Q] \Rightarrow [P \vee R \Rightarrow Q]$ is tautological, and if $P \Rightarrow Q$ and $R \Rightarrow Q$ have been stated, the tautology and two uses of Detachment would give us $P \vee R \Rightarrow Q$ anyway. We shall not confine ourselves to the above list of frequently useful ones, but shall allow ourselves the luxury of inventing inference rules like these as we go along!

> **Tautological Inference:** Whenever $P_1 \Rightarrow P_2 \Rightarrow \cdots \Rightarrow P_n \Rightarrow Q$ is tautological, then
>
> the rule $\dfrac{P_1, P_2, \ldots, P_n}{Q}$ is admissible.

Of course the tautology must be actually checked, not merely intuited. In justifying a step by this rule, the step numbers of the above-line statements must be given.

To show the power of these new procedures, we shall repeat the proof of Example 2 of § 5-9, but using, this time, an abbreviated demonstration.

$$A_1: \quad \forall xyz[x > y \land y > z \Rightarrow x > z]$$

$$A_2: \quad \forall xy[x > y \Rightarrow x \neq y]$$

$$A_1, A_2 \vdash \forall x[x > 0 \Rightarrow 0 \not> x]$$

1. $\forall xyz[x > y \land y > z \Rightarrow x > z]$	As A_1
2. $x > 0 \land 0 > x \Rightarrow x > x$	Inst $x \to x, y \to 0, z \to x$
3. $\forall xy[x > y \Rightarrow x \neq y]$	As A_2
4. $x > x \Rightarrow x \neq x$	Inst $x \to x, y \to x$
5. $x = x$	Ref Eq
6. $x > 0 \Rightarrow 0 \not> x$	Tau Inf S_2, S_4, S_5
7. $\forall x[x > 0 \Rightarrow 0 \not> x]$	Gen $\circledx$

Notice the step citations in the justification for S_6.

EXERCISES

1. Give an abbreviated demonstration for Example 1 of § 5-9 (four steps).

2. Give an abbreviated demonstration for Example 3 of § 5-9 (sixteen steps is good, thirteen is possible).

3. Consider the following argument: $[P \Rightarrow Q] \Rightarrow P \Rightarrow Q$ is tautological; therefore,

the rule $\dfrac{P \Rightarrow Q, P}{Q}$ is admissible.

If this argument is valid, why do you think the rule was omitted from the list? If it is invalid, what is wrong with it?

4. Write an abbreviated demonstration of the theorem in Exercise 9, § 5-10.

5. Write an abbreviated demonstration of the theorem in Exercise 10, § 5-10.

In Exercises 6 through 9, state whether the indicated rule is admissible under Tautological Inference. If any rule is not admissible, explain why not.

6. $\dfrac{Q \vee R, P \Leftrightarrow Q}{P \vee R}$

7. $\dfrac{P \Rightarrow Q, Q}{P}$

8. $\dfrac{P \Rightarrow Q, P \vee R, \sim Q}{\sim R}$

9. $\dfrac{Q \vee R, P \vee \sim R, \sim Q}{P}$

10. $P \vee \sim R \Rightarrow [P \Rightarrow Q] \Rightarrow R \Rightarrow Q$ is tautological. Use it to discover an inference rule
   (a) with three formulas above the line.
   (b) with two formulas above the line.
   (c) with one formula above the line.

11. Find two Tautological Inference rules not mentioned so far.

12. Find two inference rules involving quantification which have not been mentioned so far.

13. Determine which of the 21 rules given in this section can be extended as we extended rule (8), and state the extended rule in each case.

7-6 GENERALIZED VERSIONS OF CERTAIN RULES

Suppose that, in the course of a proof, we have obtained a statement

$$(1) \quad \forall xy[[x \neq y \Rightarrow xy = 1] \Rightarrow x \neq 1]$$

Suppose also, that for reasons unknown even to this author, we would like to make the statement

$$(2) \quad \forall xy[[xy \neq 1 \Rightarrow x = y] \Rightarrow x \neq 1]$$

It is true that we can state

$$(3) \quad [x \neq y \Rightarrow xy = 1] \Leftrightarrow [xy \neq 1 \Rightarrow x = y]$$

because it is a tautology, but we cannot use (3) and Biconditional Substitution on (1) to get (2), because (3) lacks the necessary universal quantifiers to make that rule work. Nor can we use Generalization to put the quantifiers on (3) without possible trouble from past or future uses of Choice or Generalization. We could state (3) with entirely different variables, chosen so as to avoid that kind of trouble, switching to the given variables as we apply Generalization, but it would be pleasant if we could, without further ado, state

$$(3') \quad \forall xy[[x \neq y \Rightarrow xy = 1] \Leftrightarrow [xy \neq 1 \Rightarrow x = y]]$$

Before giving the rule that will permit such behavior, we shall introduce a notation convenient for this and other uses.

By $\forall ZP$ we shall mean $\forall z_1 z_2 \cdots z_n P$, where $\{z_1, z_2, \ldots, z_n\}$ is merely representative of any set of variables desired.

The capital Z will always be used in this notation, but it will not always represent variables named z.

Rule of Generalized Forms: If P is a statement justifiable by any of the rules as given in Chapter 5, excepting Assumption and Detachment, then we may state $\forall ZP$.

Proof: Let the distinct variables $z_1, z_2, \ldots, z_n$ occur free in P, and let $y_1, y_2, \ldots, y_n$ be distinct variables not occurring elsewhere in the demonstration. Let Q be the statement obtained by substituting y_i for every z_i. Then we may state Q, justifying it by the same rule that would have been used for P. By virtue of the way the y_i's were chosen, we may safely use Generalization with the y_i's specified, arriving after n applications of Generalization and Detachment, at $\forall z_1 z_2 \cdots z_n P$.

With this rule, we now have the right to assert a statement such as (3'), with no preliminaries. For justification of steps of this kind, we shall merely use the name of the basic rule, in this case, "Tautology."

EXERCISE

Why are Assumption and Detachment excepted in the Rule of Generalized Forms?

Chapter 8

UNIVERSAL THEOREMS

8-1 INTRODUCTION

In Example 1 of § 5-9 we showed that

$$\exists xy[xy = yx] \vdash \exists yx[xy = yx]$$

With equal ease we can prove that

$$\exists yx[xy = yx] \vdash \exists xy[xy = yx]$$

The Biconditional Theorem now allows us to claim that there is a demonstration that

$$\vdash \exists xy[xy = yx] \Leftrightarrow \exists yx[xy = yx]$$

(In accordance with our definition of the turnstile in § 5-2, this means that no S_i in the demonstration is an assumption.)

Ostensibly, we have proved a theorem of some particular algebraic system, but if we take a second look, we see that no algebraic property was actually used; nothing was done with or to the statement $xy = yx$. The proof would be equally valid if we substituted any statement P of any mathematical system Σ for the statement $xy = yx$. (The statement would not even have to have any free occurrences of x or y.)

Let us reexamine this from the other end. Working in some mathematical system Σ, suppose we would like to prove

$$\forall z_1 z_2 \cdots z_n [\exists xyP \Leftrightarrow \exists yxP]$$

for some statement P of Σ. We know that Generalization will allow us to dress up the biconditional with universal quantifiers. To assist us in proving the naked biconditional, we would, as a matter of course, call upon the Biconditional Theorem, which will allow us to claim a proof if we can deduce each side after assuming the other side. Example 1 of § 5-9 showed how this could be done, irrespective of what statement P happened to be, and without any additional assumptions. (In Exercise 1 of § 7-5, you did it in four steps.) Thus we can state as a metatheorem for any system Σ,

> For any statement P and any variables x, y, z_1, z_2, ..., z_n, the statement $\forall z_1 z_2 \cdots z_n [\exists xyP \Leftrightarrow \exists yxP]$ is provable.

In this sense the formula $\forall Z[\exists xyP \Leftrightarrow \exists yxP]$ may be called a "universal theorem." (This is the author's terminology, not standard.)

We may want to use the theorems of Chapters 6 and 7, and other metatheorems, to prove new ones. To that end, it is essential that the metatheorems be ordered, that is, that the phrase "previous theorem" have an unambiguous meaning. As with the theorems of a mathematical system, there may be many possible orderings that will work, but we must agree upon one of them, and stick to it.

We shall take the order of presentation in the text as the official order of the theorems of Chapters 6 and 7, and of the universal theorems listed in this chapter.

8-2 SOME PARTICULARLY USEFUL UNIVERSAL THEOREMS

UT 1: $\forall Z[\forall xP \Leftrightarrow \sim\exists x\sim P]$
UT 2: $\forall Z[\sim\forall xP \Leftrightarrow \exists x\sim P]$
UT 3: $\forall Z[\forall x\sim P \Leftrightarrow \sim\exists xP]$
UT 4: $\forall Z[\sim\forall x\sim P \Leftrightarrow \exists xP]$

The first four tell the story of the relations between negation and quantification. UT 1 is an immediate consequence of the definition of the universal quantifier, which permits free substitution between $\sim\exists x\sim$ and $\forall x$.

UT 5: $\forall Z[\forall xyP \Leftrightarrow \forall yxP]$
UT 6: $\forall Z[\exists xyP \Leftrightarrow \exists yxP]$
UT 7: $\forall Z[\exists x\forall yP \Rightarrow \forall y\exists xP]$

We may allow any permutation of a string of quantifiers *of the same kind* by repeated applications of UT 5 or UT 6. Take careful note of the fact that UT 7 is not a biconditional.

UT 8: $\forall Z[\forall xP(x) \Leftrightarrow \forall yP(y)]$
UT 9: $\forall Z[\exists xP(x) \Leftrightarrow \exists yP(y)]$

With the help of Biconditional Substitution, UT 8 and UT 9 allow changes of variable, as suggested in § 4-8. They have obvious extensions to any number of variables. The remaining rules all deal with the act of distributing quantifiers over binary sentential operators. Again, please notice that only UT 10 and UT 11 are biconditionals.

UT 10: $\forall Z[\forall x[P \wedge Q] \Leftrightarrow \forall xP \wedge \forall xQ]$
UT 11: $\forall Z[\exists x[P \vee Q] \Leftrightarrow \exists xP \vee \exists xQ]$
UT 12: $\forall Z[\forall xP \vee \forall xQ \Rightarrow \forall x[P \vee Q]]$
UT 13: $\forall Z[\exists x[P \wedge Q] \Rightarrow \exists xP \wedge \exists xQ]$
UT 14: $\forall Z[\forall x[P \Rightarrow Q] \Rightarrow [\forall xP \Rightarrow \forall xQ]]$
UT 15: $\forall Z[[\exists xP \Rightarrow \exists xQ] \Rightarrow \exists x[P \Rightarrow Q]]$
UT 16: $\forall Z[\forall x[P \Leftrightarrow Q] \Rightarrow [\forall xP \Leftrightarrow \forall xQ]]$

EXERCISES

1. (a) Show that the statements

P: x is even
Q: x is odd

furnish a counterexample for the converse of UT 12, the universe of discourse being the integers.
(b) Try these statements on the converse of UT 13.

2. (a) Find a counterexample in the real numbers to the converse of UT 12.
(b) Try the same statements on the converse of UT 13.
(c) Will it always work out that any statements furnishing a counterexample to the converse of UT 12 will automatically give you a counterexample to UT 13? Discuss.

3. Find a mathematical and a nonmathematical counterexample to the converse of UT 14.

4. Find a mathematical and a nonmathematical counterexample to the converse of UT 15.

5. Find a mathematical and a nonmathematical counterexample to the converse of UT 16.

8-3 EQUALITY AS AN EQUIVALENCE RELATION

We are not going to define "relation" in this text, but you may use the informal idea that a symbol, for example, R, represents a binary relation in a system Σ if there are terms α and β such that α R β is an atomic statement in Σ (not necessarily provable).

There are three properties of equality which almost characterize it as a relation. They are **reflexivity, symmetry,** and **transitivity.** These ideas were introduced in § 5-10. We now restate the definition of an equivalence relation.

A binary relation R in a system Σ is an **equivalence relation in a set S** if and only if

> i. $\forall x[x \text{ R } x]$ (Reflexivity)
> ii. $\forall xy[x \text{ R } y \Rightarrow y \text{ R } x]$ (Symmetry)
> iii. $\forall xyz[x \text{ R } y \wedge y \text{ R } z \Rightarrow x \text{ R } z]$ (Transitivity)

are all provable in Σ, with x, y, and z restricted to elements of S.

The total content of the Rule of Reflexivity of Equality is the fact that equality is reflexive in any system. The other properties are stated in the following theorems, whose proofs we leave to you.

> UT 17A: $\forall Z[\alpha = \beta \Rightarrow \beta = \alpha]$
>   17B: $\forall Z[\alpha = \beta \Leftrightarrow \beta = \alpha]$
> UT 18: $\forall Z[[\alpha = \beta] \wedge [\beta = \gamma] \Rightarrow \alpha = \gamma]$

Although 17A appears weaker in form than 17B, it is actually equivalent to it. See Exercise 6 of § 5-10.

8-4 FORMAL PROOF

Let T be a theorem of Σ. A **formal proof of** T will be an argument showing that $A_1, A_2, \ldots, A_n \vdash T$, where the A_i's are the postulates and definitions of Σ. This argument is to consist of:

1. Abbreviated demonstrations of any statements of the system, using any assumptions desired. (The assumptions must also be statements of the system.)

2. Applications of the theorems of Chapter 6. By virtue of the Lemma Theorem, all previously proved theorems of Σ, and any instance of a universal theorem (that is, with particular statements in the place of sentential variables), are admissible in the demonstration-like proofs described above, without specifically listing them as assumptions.

One may also omit listing which particular postulates and definitions of Σ are to be used, because the final result allows any or all of them as assumptions. On the other hand, any statement with free variables must be explicitly listed as an assumption of a demonstration if it is to be so used, to ensure proper application of the Lemma Theorem, and also proper use of Choice and Generalization. Part 1 of this definition may seem rather overpermissive, but the structure of the Lemma Theorem will prevent circular reasoning.

To prove a universal theorem, we must establish that a certain demonstration exists, whatever statement(s) are put in the place of the sentential variables. We cannot produce the actual demonstration, since we use sentential variables in place of statements in framing the universal theorems. Example 1 of § 5-9 was an actual demonstration, but as soon as we replace $xy = yx$ by P, to show that we can go through the same paces without any reference to the content of the statement involved, it is no longer a demonstration, it is a **demonstration scheme**. Hence, in a formal proof of a universal theorem, abbreviated demonstration schemes replace the abbreviated demonstrations of actual statements. Otherwise, they follow the definition just given for the formal proof of a theorem of a system Σ. As illustrations, we shall give formal proofs of UT 10 and UT 11.

To prove UT 10, we shall use the Biconditional Theorem, so we start with a proof that $\forall x[P \wedge Q] \vdash \forall xP \wedge \forall xQ$. It will be necessary to change variables in the course of this proof, so we shall choose a new variable, say

x', and write P' and Q' for the statements obtained from P and Q, respectively, by substituting x' for every free occurrence (if any) of x in those statements, just as in the proof of the Lemma Theorem. Justifications are fairly obvious, and have been left as an exercise.

$$x[P \wedge Q] \vdash \forall xP \wedge \forall xQ$$

Proof

1. $\forall x[P \wedge Q]$

2. $P \wedge Q$

3. P

4. $P' \wedge Q'$

5. Q'

6. $\forall xP$

7. $\forall xQ$

8. $\forall xP \wedge \forall xQ$

We now interchange the roles of the given and proved statements.

$$\forall xP \wedge \forall xQ \vdash \forall x[P \wedge Q]$$

Proof

1. $\forall xP \wedge \forall xQ$

2. $\forall xP$

3. $\forall xQ$

4. P

5. Q

6. $P \wedge Q$

7. $\forall x[P \wedge Q]$

On the strength of these two proofs and the Biconditional Theorem, we can now claim that there is a demonstration that

$$\vdash \forall x[P \wedge Q] \Leftrightarrow \forall xP \wedge \forall xQ$$

Since no variables that were specified in the lemmas can occur free in the last formula, we could continue the demonstration whose existence we have proved with as many steps of Generalization as we wish, which justifies prefixing $\forall Z$, thus giving us a proof of UT 10.

The next example, UT 11, is most easily proved by using previous universal theorems.

$$\text{UT 11:} \quad \forall Z[\exists x[P \vee Q] \Leftrightarrow \exists x P \vee \exists x Q]$$

Proof

1. $\forall x[\sim P \wedge \sim Q] \Leftrightarrow \forall x \sim P \wedge \forall x \sim Q$	UT 10
2. $\forall x[[\sim P \wedge \sim Q] \Leftrightarrow \sim[P \vee Q]]$	Tau
3. $\forall x \sim [P \vee Q] \Leftrightarrow \forall x \sim P \wedge \forall x \sim Q$	Bi Sub
4. $\forall x \sim [P \vee Q] \Leftrightarrow \sim \exists x[P \vee Q]$	UT 3
5. $\forall x \sim P \Leftrightarrow \sim \exists x P$	UT 3
6. $\forall x \sim Q \Leftrightarrow \sim \exists x Q$	UT 3
7. $\exists x[P \vee Q] \Leftrightarrow \exists x P \vee \exists x Q$	Tau Inf S_3
	$S_4,\ S_5,\ S_6$

As before, we can now use as many steps of Generalization as we wish, which justifies the prefixing of $\forall Z$.

Step 1 does not have the exact form in which UT 10 was stated. Since the sentential variables in a universal theorem stand for *any* statement of a system, they may be replaced consistently by any other sentential formula. Notice also the use of a generalized tautology in step 2. The proofs of many universal theorems can be shortened by tricks such as these. For example, UT 4 can be proved (up to $\forall Z$) in two steps!

EXERCISES

1. Supply the missing reasons in the proof of UT 10.

2. Write out and test the tautology used in S_7 in the proof of UT 11. Substitute sentential variables for formulas as follows:

$$R: \quad \forall x \sim [P \vee Q] \qquad U: \quad \exists x P$$
$$S: \quad \exists x[P \vee Q] \qquad V: \quad \forall x \sim Q$$
$$T: \quad \forall x \sim P \qquad\quad W: \quad \exists x Q$$

3. **(a)** Why is it necessary to use Instance twice, with different variables, in the first part of the proof of UT 10?
   (b) Can you find another proof that $\forall x[P \wedge Q] \vdash \forall x P \wedge \forall z Q$ which does not require a change of variables? (The Conjunction Theorem is relevant here.)

4. Give a formal proof of UT 3.

5. Give a formal proof of UT 4.

6. Give a formal proof of UT 5.

7. Give a formal proof of UT 7.

8. Give a formal proof of UT 8.

9. Give a formal proof of UT 9.

10. Give a formal proof of UT 12.

11. Give a formal proof of UT 13.

12. Give a formal proof of UT 14.

13. Give a formal proof of UT 15.

14. Prove UT 16 in one step.

15. Give a formal proof of UT 17A and UT 17B (use Equality Substitution).

16. Give a formal proof of UT 18.

17. The first four universal theorems can be extended to cover any number of variables.
    (a) Prove: $\vdash \forall xy P \Leftrightarrow {\sim}\exists xy {\sim} P$.
    (b) Prove UT 4 for two variables.

18. **(a)** Prove: If there are no free occurrences of x in Q, then $\vdash \forall Z[\forall x[Q \Rightarrow P] \Rightarrow [Q \Rightarrow \forall x P]$.
    (b) At what step of your proof was the restriction on Q necessary?

19. (a) Prove: If there are no free occurrences of x in Q, then $\vdash \forall Z[[Q \Rightarrow \forall xP] \Rightarrow \forall x[Q \Rightarrow P]]$.

(b) At what step in this proof did the restriction on Q come into the picture?

20. Find counterexamples to the theorems of Exercises 18 and 19, if the restriction on Q is violated.

(There are a number of theorems like those in Exercises 18 and 19, allowing the shifting of quantifiers around substatements which they do not affect. Perhaps you can think of some others.)

8-5 APPLICATIONS IN GROUP THEORY

For additional practice with formal proof, we now turn to the mathematical system known as a "group." A group is a set of elements together with a binary operator (which we shall denote by "$*$") satisfying certain axioms. There are several equivalent sets of axioms for a group. Perhaps the axiom set most frequently used is the following set of four.

Closure: For any x and y in S, $x * y$ is a uniquely defined element of S.

Associativity: For any x, y, and z in S, $(x * y) * z = x * (y * z)$.

Identity Element: There exists one and only one u in S such that for any x in S, $x * u = x$ and $u * x = x$.

Inverse Element: For each element x in S there exists one and only one element y in S such that $x * y = u$ and $y * x = u$.

The last two axioms can be given in a weaker form, postulating existence but not uniqueness. Uniqueness can then be proved with a theorem.

Instead of precisely this set of axioms, we shall use another set, equivalent to it in the sense that every axiom or theorem of either system is an axiom or theorem of the other. In stating our axioms formally, we shall omit all mention of S, for it will be understood that all terms represent elements of S.

We shall also omit the closure axiom. In its place, we shall agree that, in addition to the variables, any expression of the form $\alpha * \beta$ is a term whenever

α and β are terms. We shall also follow the usual algebraic practice of identifying $(\alpha * \beta)$ with $\alpha * \beta$ in forming complex terms.

Let us now proceed to a formal presentation of the system, in accordance with the description given in § 5-1.

1. *Undefined Expressions.* The binary operator $*$, and, as variables, lowercase Latin letters. However, the letter u will be reserved for a constant, to be defined later. The only terms will be variables, constants, and expressions constructed from simpler terms by use of the binary operator.

2. The only atomic forms will be those stating the equality of two terms.

3. *Axioms.*

Axiom 1: $\forall xyz[(x * y) * z = x * (y * z)]$ (Associativity)
      2: $\forall xy[\exists z[x * z = y] \wedge \exists w[w * x = y]]$ (Right and Left
                                            Divisibility)

The second axiom replaces both the identity element axiom and the inverse element axiom. It also points up the fact that $*$ has not been assumed to be commutative; $z * x$ does not necessarily equal $x * z$.

In a system using the identity element and inverse element statements as axioms, Axiom 2 would be a theorem. In our system, the identity element statement will be Theorem 2, and the inverse element statement will be Theorem 4.

In some places, it will be convenient to have Axiom 2 split into two separate statements. This is our first theorem.

Theorem 1a: $\forall xy\exists z[x * z = y]$
        1b: $\forall xy\exists w[w * x = y]$

Proof of Theorem 1a

1. $\forall xy[\exists z[x * z = y] \wedge \exists w[w * x = y]]$ $\quad\quad\Big\|$ As A_2

2. $S_1 \Leftrightarrow \forall xy\exists z[x * z = y] \wedge \forall xy\exists w[w * x = y]$ $\;\Big\|$ UT 11

3. $\forall xy\exists z[x * z = y]$ $\quad\quad\quad\quad\quad\quad\quad\quad\quad\Big\|$ Tau Inf S_1, S_2

The proof of Theorem 1b follows the same pattern.

The proof of the next theorem is rather long. All justifications have been given, but it would be a good idea to cover them as you study the proof, to see whether you can furnish the justifications yourself. As stated before, this theorem is the identity element statement.

Theorem 2: $\exists_1 z \forall x [x * z = x \land z * x = x]$

For convenience, we shall use a predicate variable to abbreviate the statement in the brackets, as follows:

$$P(x, z) \quad \text{for} \quad [x * z = x \land z * x = x]$$

Then Theorem 2 can be written

$$\exists_1 z \forall x P(x, z)$$

or, using the first version of $\exists_1$ given in the exercises of § 5-9,

$$\exists z [\forall x P(x, z) \land \forall y [\forall x P(x, y) \Rightarrow y = z]]$$

This will be our target.

Proof: Noticing that $P(x, z)$ looks suggestively like Axiom 2 if the y of that statement is changed to an x, we start with Axiom 2 and use the Rule of Instance.

1. $\forall xy [\exists z [x * z = y] \land \exists w [w * x = y]]$	As A_2
2. $\exists z [x * z = x] \land \exists w [w * x = x]$	Inst $x \to x, y \to x$

With our eye still on $P(x, z)$, we see that we have to remove the existential quantifier from the individual parts of S_2. To do so, we separate the parts.

3. $\exists z [x * z = x]$	Tau Inf S_2
4. $\exists w [w * x = x]$	Tau Inf S_2
5. $x * p = x$	Ch $\circled{p}$, x
6. $q * x = x$	Ch $\circled{q}$, x

The reason for the change of variable in S_5 will appear shortly. It would have made life easier if we could have specified p in S_6 also, but that was not possible (why?), so we shall have to use other methods to show that p and q are equal. A trick that works is to show that both are equal to $q * p$. To do this, we choose an element r such that $r * x = q$ (using Th 1b) and an element s such that $x * t = p$ (using Th 1a). Then we take steps which, in effect, "multiply" each member of the equation in S_5 on the left by r, and on the right in S_6 by s. With the help of the associative law, we obtain $q * p = q$ and $q * p = p$.

7. $\forall xy \exists w[w * x = y]$	Th 1b†
8. $\exists w[w * x = q]$	Inst $x \to x$, $y \to q$
9. $r * x = q$	Ch $\widehat{r}$, x, q
10. $\forall xy \exists z[x * z = x]$	Th 1a
11. $\exists z[x * z = p]$	Inst $x \to x$, $y \to p$
12. $x * s = p$	Ch $\widehat{s}$, x, p

Steps 8 and 11 are the ones that made it necessary to change variables in steps 5 and 6. If we had specified z at step 5, we would have been in trouble at step 11, because we could not have used $y \to z$ without violating a restriction on Instance (which one?).

We have no theorem for "multiplication of equations," but we can obtain the same result with the help of A_1.

13. $\forall xyz[(x * y) * z = x * (y * z)]$	As A_1
14. $(r * x) * p = r * (x * p)$	Inst $x \to r$, $y \to x$, $z \to p$
15. $(r * x) * p = r * x$	Eq Sub S_5, S_{14}
16. $q * p = q$	Eq Sub S_9, S_{15}
17. $(q * x) * s = q * (x * s)$	Inst S_{13}, $x \to q$, $y \to x$, $z \to s$
18. $x * s = q * (x * s)$	Eq Sub S_6, S_{17}
19. $p = q * p$	Eq Sub S_{12}, S_{18}
20. $p = q$	Eq Sub S_{16}, S_{19}
21. $p * x = x$	Eq Sub S_{20}, S_6

We could now get $P(x, p)$ from S_5 and S_{21}. Referring to our target, we see that there would be little trouble in swapping the p for a z when the existential quantifier is finally prefixed, but first we must generalize on the x, and the presence of p bars this (why?). However, if $P(x, p)$ is

† We shall use this abbreviation for referring to theorems in the justification column.

in fact generalizable, it should be possible to do so with some other variable in place of x, one that has not been guilty of associating with a specified variable. Indeed, we can choose a new variable, say t, and immediately assert

22. $P(t, p) \Rightarrow \forall x P(x, p)$ || Gen $\textcircled{t}, p$

(There is a good reason for not postponing this step.) Now we must show that p is also an identity element for t; in symbols, $P(t, p)$. We do so by going back to the equations in S_5 and S_{21}, and exchanging the x for t by multiplying on the left and right, respectively, by suitably chosen elements. The procedure will be much like that of steps 7 through 19.

23. $\exists w[w * x = t]$ || Inst S_7, $x \to x$, $y \to t$

24. $j * x = t$ || Ch $\textcircled{j}$, x, t

Can you see how this step would have caused trouble if S_{22} had been postponed?

25. $\exists z[x * z = t]$ || Inst S_{10}, $x \to x$, $y \to t$

26. $x * k = t$ || Ch $\textcircled{k}$, x, t

27. $(j * x) * p = j * (x * p)$ || Inst S_{13}, $x \to j$, $y \to x$, $z \to p$

28. $(j * x) * p = j * x$ || Eq Sub S_5, S_{27}

29. $t * p = t$ || Eq Sub S_{24}, S_{28}

30. $(p * x) * k = p * (x * k)$ || Inst S_{13}, $x \to p$, $y \to x$, $z \to k$

31. $x * k = p * (x * k)$ || Eq Sub S_{21}, S_{30}

32. $t = p * t$ || Eq Sub S_{26}, S_{31}

S_{32} is in reversed order for our purposes, but we have a universal theorem to fix that.

33. $t = p * t \Leftrightarrow p * t = t$ || UT 17B

We could now assert $P(t, p)$, but we can skip right to

34. $\forall x P(x, p)$ $\qquad\qquad\qquad$ ‖ Tau Inf $S_{22}, S_{29}, S_{32}, S_{33}$

This gives us the first part of the target statement. We must now show that any element, say y, that behaves like p is, in fact, p itself. We start with the assumption that y behaves that way.

† ⎡ 35. $\forall x P(x, y)$ $\qquad\qquad\qquad$ ‖ Temp As

  | 36. $P(p, y)$ $\qquad\qquad\qquad\qquad$ ‖ Inst $x \rightarrow p$

  | 37. $y * p = p$ $\qquad\qquad\qquad\quad$ ‖ Tau Inf S_{36}

  | 38. $P(y, p)$ $\qquad\qquad\qquad\qquad$ ‖ Inst $S_{34}, x \rightarrow y$

  | 39. $y * p = y$ $\qquad\qquad\qquad\quad$ ‖ Tau Inf S_{38}

  ⎣ 40. $p = y$ $\qquad\qquad\qquad\qquad$ ‖ Eq Sub S_{37}, S_{39}

41. $\forall x P(x, y) \Rightarrow p = y$ $\qquad\quad$ ‖ Ded Th

42. $\forall y [\forall x P(x, y) \Rightarrow p = y]$ $\qquad$ ‖ Gen ⓨ, p

This is the second piece of the target. It only remains to put them together and prefix a quantifier.

43. $\forall x P(x, p) \wedge \forall y [\forall x P(x, y) \Rightarrow p = y]$ $\quad$ ‖ Tau Inf S_{34}, S_{42}

44. $\exists z [\forall x P(x, z) \wedge \forall y [\forall x P(x, y) \Rightarrow z = y]]$ $\quad$ ‖ Exam. $p \rightarrow z$

Theorem 2 permits us to define a constant, since it asserts the unique existence of a certain mathematical object (see § 10-6).

Definition

$$u: \forall y [y = u \Leftrightarrow \forall x P(x, y)]$$

As a corollary to the definition we have

Theorem 3: $\forall x P(x, u)$

Proof: Exercise 5.

† For an explanation of this long bracket, see the next to last paragraph of § 6-3.

With an identity element such as u in existence, any element y such that $y * x = u$ is called a **left inverse of** x. If $x * z = u$, then z is a **right inverse of** x. Of course, if the binary operation is commutative, then every right inverse is automatically a left inverse, and vice versa. An element that is both a right and left inverse of x is called a **two-sided inverse**, or, simply, an **inverse of** x. Theorem 4 asserts the existence of a unique inverse for each element.

Theorem 4: $\forall x \exists_1 y [x * y = u \wedge y * x = u]$

We shall again use a predicate variable to shorten this formula. Let us write

$$Q(x, y) \quad \text{for} \quad [x * y = u \wedge y * x = u]$$

Then Theorem 4 may be written

$$\forall x \exists_1 y Q(x, y)$$

or, in disabbreviated form,

$$\forall x \exists y [Q(x, y) \wedge \forall z [Q(x, z) \Rightarrow y = z]]$$

To help us with this theorem, we first prove the following

Lemma: $\forall y w [x * y = u \wedge w * x = u \Rightarrow y = w]$

This lemma is of some interest in itself. In effect, it says that in a system with an identity element, no element can have distinct left and right inverses. In other words, if a left inverse of x is not also a right inverse, then x has no right inverse. Since only Axiom 1 is used in the proof, the lemma applies to a much wider class of systems than groups.

We have left all the justifications as an exercise.

Proof of Lemma

1. $x * y = u \wedge w * x = u$

2. $x * y = u$

3. $w * x = u$

Informally, if we could multiply S_2 on the left by w, and S_3 on the right by y, we would get $\dot{w} * (x * y) = w * u$ and $(w * x) * y = u * y$. By the associative law and the basic properties of u (Theorem 3), this would show that $w = y$. Our formal device for accomplishing this, as before, starts with the associative law.

4. $\forall xyz[(x * y) * z = x * (y * z)]$

5. $(w * x) * y = w * (x * y)$

6. $u * y = w * (x * y)$

7. $u * y = w * u$

Now we bring in the special nature of the constant u.

8. $\forall x[x * u = x \wedge u * x = x]$

9. $y * u = y \wedge u * y = y$

10. $u * y = y$

11. $w * u = w \wedge u * w = w$

12. $w * u = w$

13. $y = w * u$

14. $y = w$

15. $x * y = u \wedge w * x = u \Rightarrow y = w$

16. $\forall w S_{15}$

17. $\forall yw S_{15}$

We have proved that

$$A_1 \vdash \text{Lemma}$$

We now go on to prove that

$$\text{Lemma}, A_2 \vdash \text{Th 4}$$

Proof of Theorem: Our first task is to show that any given x has a left and a right inverse, so that we may apply the lemma.

1. $\forall xy[\exists z[x * z = y] \wedge \exists w[w * x = y]]$

2. $\exists z[x * z = u] \wedge \exists w[w * x = u]$

3. $\exists z[x * z = u]$

4. $x * y = u$ Ch $\textcircled{y}$, x

5. $\exists w[w * x = u]$

6. $w * x = u$

Steps 4 and 6 establish the two inverses of x. We now use the lemma.

7. $\forall yw[x * y = u \wedge w * x = u \Rightarrow y = w]$

8. $x * y = u \wedge w * x = u \Rightarrow y = w$

9. $y = w$

10. $y * x = u$

Steps 4 and 10 show that we now have an inverse for x. Their conjunction is, in fact, $Q(x, y)$. Looking at the target for this theorem, we see that we still need to show that whenever $Q(x, z)$, then $y = z$.

11. $x * z = u \wedge z * x = u$

12. $x * y = u \wedge z * x = u \Rightarrow y = z$ Inst S_7

13. $y = z$ Tau Inf

14. $x * z = u \wedge z * x = u \Rightarrow y = z$

15. $\forall z[Q(x, z) \Rightarrow y = z]$

16. $Q(x, y) \wedge \forall z[Q(x, z) \Rightarrow y = z]$

17. $\exists y[Q(x, y) \wedge \forall z[Q(x, z) \Rightarrow y = z]]$

18. $\forall x \exists y[Q(x, y) \wedge \forall z[Q(x, z) \Rightarrow y = z]]$

On the basis of these two proofs, after making appropriate checks (see Exercise 2), we can invoke the Lemma Theorem and assert

$$A_1, A_2 \vdash \text{Th } 4$$

Theorem 4 permits us to define a term containing one free variable.

Definition

$$x^{-1}: \forall xy[y = x^{-1} \Leftrightarrow x * y = u \land y * x = u]$$

As with the definition of u, this one has a useful corollary.

Theorem 5: $\forall x[x * x^{-1} = u \land x^{-1} * x = u]$

EXERCISES

1. (a) If we take S to be the positive real numbers, and the operation $*$ to be ordinary multiplication, verify that we have a group.
   (b) Using this interpretation, justify the name given to A_2.
   (c) Show that in this interpretation, S cannot be enlarged to include all the real numbers.
   (d) Verify that if the operation is taken to be ordinary addition, then S can be all the real numbers.
   (e) Again with addition as the operation, find a proper subset of the real numbers (that is, not the whole set) which forms a group.

2. What are the "appropriate checks" mentioned in the proof of Theorem 4? Write out your verification that everything is in order.

3. Furnish the justifications for the proof of the lemma for Theorem 4.

4. Furnish the justifications for the proof of Theorem 4.

5. Prove Theorem 3. Reflexivity of Equality will be useful.

6. Prove Theorem 5.

7. Prove Theorem 6: $\forall xy[x * y = u \Rightarrow y = x^{-1}]$. This theorem asserts that in a group, any right inverse of x is *the* inverse of x.

8. Prove Theorem 7: $\forall xy[(x * y)^{-1} = (y^{-1}) * (x^{-1})]$. (The inverse of a "product" is the product of the inverses *in reverse order*.) [*Suggestion:* Apply A_1, Theorem 3, and Theorem 5 to the term $(x * y) * ((y^{-1}) * (x^{-1}))$.]

9. **(a)** Prove Theorem 8a: $\forall xyz[x = y \Rightarrow x * z = y * z]$. (*Suggestion:* Start with the statement $x * z = x * z$.)

(b) Prove the converse, Theorem 8b: $\forall xyz[x * z = y * z \Rightarrow x = y]$ (*Suggestion:* Use Instance on Theorem 8a, with $x \to x * z$, $y \to y * z$, $z \to z^{-1}$.)

(c) Prove Theorem 8: $\forall xyz[x = y \Leftrightarrow x * z = y * z]$.

(d) Theorem 8b is sometimes called the "right cancellation law." What would the "left cancellation law" be?

10. **(a)** Prove Theorem 9: $\forall xyzw[x = y \land z = w \Rightarrow x * z = y * w]$.

(b) With S and $*$ interpreted as in Exercise 1, give a common informal statement of this theorem.

Chapter 9

TECHNIQUES OF NEGATION

9-1 MOTIVATION

We interrupt our development of the logical theory for a brief chapter aimed at developing your technique in a frequently used operation.

When a mathematician has become discouraged in his attempts to prove a generalized conjecture $\forall x C$, and has begun to suspect that the conjecture is false, the professional thing for him to do is to look for a counterexample. That is, he tries to prove $\exists x \sim C$, which is equivalent to $\sim \forall x C$.

If he succeeds in the latter course, he can turn his pursuit to tamer geese than the original conjecture. On the other hand, after several unsuccessful attempts to construct counterexamples, he might go back to his attempts at proving $\forall x C$ with renewed hope, and, perhaps, with a few new ideas for possible lines of attack.

A line that might well result from a search for counterexamples is the method of indirect proof, or reductio ad absurdum. There are many varieties of indirect proof,† but a feature characteristic of all of them is the assuming of the negation of the theorem to be proved.

Suppose that we have defined a certain set S of real numbers, and wish to prove

Every member of S has a next larger number in the set.

(This is true, for example, of the set of all integers, but not true of the set of all rational numbers.) Suppose also that we have decided to use an indirect proof. It is not very helpful to start with

Not every member of S has a next larger number in the set.

---

† See, for example, J. B. Rosser, *Logic for Mathematicians* (New York: McGraw-Hill, 1953), pp. 34, 35.

There is not much that can be done directly in the way of formal logic with that form for the negation. We must apply a definition of "next larger" to obtain a less abbreviated form of the proposed theorem, to see what ammunition its negation provides. The proposed theorem might then read:

> For every x in S, there is a y in S such that $y > x$, and such that for any z in S, if $z > x$, then $z \not< y$.

Now what? Can you write a technically useful form for the negation of this conjecture? Before proceeding further, try it now.

* * *

An acceptable form will be found further on. At this point it may encourage you to learn that the problem of negation can be brought down to a crank-turning level.

9-2 THE BASIC RELATIONS AND THEIR APPLICATIONS

There are just a few basic formulas to learn: the two biconditionals listed as UT 2 and UT 3, repeated below for reference, and the truth-table tautologies listed after them. $\forall Z$ should be prefixed to all of them; it has been omitted to make the essential relationships stand out more clearly.

$$(1)\quad \sim\forall x P \Leftrightarrow \exists x \sim P$$
$$(2)\quad \sim\exists x P \Leftrightarrow \forall x \sim P$$
$$(3)\quad \sim\sim P \Leftrightarrow P$$
$$(4a)\quad \sim[P \wedge Q] \Leftrightarrow [\sim P \vee \sim Q]$$
$$(4b)\quad \sim[P \wedge Q] \Leftrightarrow [P \Rightarrow \sim Q]$$
$$(4c)\quad \sim[P \wedge Q] \Leftrightarrow [Q \Rightarrow \sim P]$$
$$(5)\quad \sim[P \vee Q] \Leftrightarrow [\sim P \wedge \sim Q]$$
$$(6)\quad \sim[P \Rightarrow Q] \Leftrightarrow [P \wedge \sim Q]$$
$$(7a)\quad \sim[P \Leftrightarrow Q] \Leftrightarrow [P \Leftrightarrow \sim Q]$$
$$(7b)\quad \sim[P \Leftrightarrow Q] \Leftrightarrow [\sim P \Leftrightarrow Q]$$

Given any sentential formula properly constructed out of sentential variables, sentential operators, and quantifiers, we can convert the formula into a logically equivalent one ·in which the tildes are attached only to sentential variables. When a formula has that property, we shall say that it is in "negation-reduced form." Note that $\sim\sim P$ is not in negation-reduced form, since it is an abbreviation for $\sim[\sim P]$. The choices offered in (4) and (7) indicate that there may be more than one negation-reduced form for a given formula.

To see how the basic formulas work, let us start with the formula

$$(8) \quad \exists x \forall y P \vee \forall x [P \Rightarrow \exists y [Q \vee R \Leftrightarrow \sim[S \wedge R]]]$$

The negation of this could be written

$$(9) \quad \sim[\exists x \forall y P \vee \forall x [P \Rightarrow \exists y [Q \vee R \Leftrightarrow \sim[S \wedge R]]]]$$

This is a solid chunk of formula, quite indigestible to the gastric processes of logic without the enzymatic action of formulas (1) through (7). For the first reduction we use (5), since the governing operation within the outermost brackets of (9) is that of disjunction. To help focus your attention on the sites of action, we shall put down only the significant parts of the formula at each stage.

$$\sim\exists x \forall y P \wedge \sim\forall x [P \Rightarrow \cdots$$

Next we use (1) and (2) to move the tildes past the quantifiers.

$$\forall x \exists y \sim P \wedge \exists x \sim[P \Rightarrow \exists y[\cdots$$

We are finished with the left half of the original disjunction, but we shall not stop until any tilde remaining is attached to a single sentential variable. For the next step we use (6).

$$\cdots P \wedge \exists x [P \wedge \sim\exists y [Q \cdots$$

Again using (2),

$$\cdots [P \wedge \forall y \sim[Q \vee R \Leftrightarrow \sim[S \wedge R]]]$$

With the use of (7) and (3), we finally arrive at

$$(10) \quad \forall x \exists y \sim P \wedge \exists x [P \wedge \forall y [Q \vee R \Leftrightarrow S \wedge R]]$$

The claim that (10) is more digestible than (9), logically speaking, is based upon the availability of much smaller substatements. Taking (10) as a statement S_i of a proof, we can get successively:

i. $\forall x \exists y \sim P \wedge \exists x[P \wedge \forall y[Q \vee R \Leftrightarrow S \wedge R]]$

$i + 1.$ $\forall x \exists y \sim P$	Tau Inf
$i + 2.$ $\exists y \sim P$	Inst
$i + 3.$ $\sim P'$	Ch
$i + 4.$ $\exists x[P \wedge \forall y[Q \vee R \Leftrightarrow S \wedge R]]$	Tau Inf S_i
$i + 5.$ $P'' \wedge \forall y[Q' \vee R' \Leftrightarrow S' \wedge R']$	Ch
$i + 6.$ P''	Tau Inf
$i + 7.$ $\forall y[Q' \vee R' \Leftrightarrow S' \wedge R']$	Tau Inf
$i + 8.$ $Q' \vee R' \Leftrightarrow S' \wedge R'$	Inst

P', P'', Q', R', and S' have been introduced here because the restrictions on the Rule of Choice might have forced a change of variable when that rule was used.

To carry out the same procedure with the last statement given in § 9-1, we shall first rewrite it with purified quantifiers (see § 4-3).

$$\forall x[x \in S \Rightarrow \exists y[y \in S \wedge y > x \wedge \forall z[z \in S \Rightarrow [z > x \Rightarrow z \not< y]]]]$$

We'll let you practice on this one; a final result could be

$$\exists x[x \in S \wedge \forall y[y \in S \Rightarrow y > x \Rightarrow \exists z[z \in S \wedge z > x \wedge z < y]]]$$

(Some variation is possible here.) Translating back, using modified quantifiers, this reads

> There is an x in S such that for any y in S, if $y > x$, then there is a z in S such that $z > x$ and $z < y$.

For those who wish to develop speed at this frequently necessary chore, there is one more point we should make—we do not have to purify quantifiers to arrive at the final form shown above. "There is an x with property p, such that S holds" is purified in "There is an x such that x has property p and S holds." Symbolically, this is $\exists x[P \wedge S]$. Its negation could be written $\forall x[P \Rightarrow \sim S]$, translated, "For every x, if x has property p, then S does not hold." This is precisely what we described in §4-3 as the purified form of "For every x with property p, S does not hold." Thus we can, in effect, ignore "with property p" in forming the negation.

EXERCISES

Write the negation for each formula in negation-reduced form. (Add brackets where needed.)

1. $P \vee Q \Rightarrow P \wedge R$

2. $S \vee {\sim}T \Leftrightarrow T \Rightarrow S$

3. $[S \Rightarrow P] \vee [P \vee S]$

4. $P \Rightarrow Q \Rightarrow R \Rightarrow S \Rightarrow T$

5. $\forall x \exists y [P \wedge Q]$

6. $\forall x P \Rightarrow \exists x Q$

7. $\forall xy P \Rightarrow \exists x [\exists y P \Rightarrow Q]$

8. $\forall x [\forall y P \Leftrightarrow \exists yzt [{\sim}R \vee S]]$

9. $\exists x [P \Rightarrow \forall y Q \wedge \forall z R \wedge \exists z S]$

10. $\forall x [P \vee \exists z {\sim} R] \Rightarrow \exists z R \Rightarrow \forall x {\sim} P$

11. Consider the formula

$$P \Leftrightarrow Q \Leftrightarrow R \Leftrightarrow S$$

There are several negation-reduced forms logically equivalent to this, which differ from it only by the addition of a tilde to two or more sentential variables. For example, since ${\sim}R \Leftrightarrow {\sim}S$ is logically equivalent to $R \Leftrightarrow S$, we can assert that the given formula is logically equivalent to

$$P \Leftrightarrow Q \Leftrightarrow {\sim}R \Leftrightarrow {\sim}S$$

(a) List three more equivalent forms and give some argument to support your claim of equivalence.

(b) How many are there in all, counting the given one?

(c) How many negation-reduced formulas are there logically equivalent to the negation of the given one?

(d) Answer (b) and (c) for the formula

$$P \Leftrightarrow Q \Leftrightarrow R.$$

(e) How many are there for the formula

$$P_1 \Leftrightarrow P_2 \Leftrightarrow \cdots \Leftrightarrow P_n?$$

Give some argument to support your contention.

12. Skill in writing negations helps in discovering useful equivalent forms for assumed or proved statements by exploiting the equivalence of $P \Rightarrow Q$ with $\sim Q \Rightarrow \sim P$, and of $\sim P \Leftrightarrow \sim Q$ with $P \Leftrightarrow Q$. It will not be stretching the customary usage too much if we refer to each of these pairs as "contrapositives" (usually reserved for the first pair). The proof given for UT 11 in Chapter 8 uses the fact that UT 10 and UT 11 are contrapositives.

(a) Write the contrapositive of each of the universal Theorems 5 through 16, in negation-reduced form.

(b) In which cases do you get a universal theorem that looks significantly different from those already on the list?

13. The formula $P \wedge Q \Rightarrow R$ has $\sim R \Rightarrow \sim P \vee \sim Q$ as its negation-reduced contrapositive (see Exercise 12). It is frequently productive to use the partial contrapositives $P \wedge \sim R \Rightarrow \sim Q$ and $Q \wedge \sim R \Rightarrow \sim P$.

(a) Verify that the given partial contrapositives are each equivalent to $P \wedge Q \Rightarrow R$.

(b) By contraposition, and partial contraposition, obtain three statements each logically equivalent to

If n is divisible by 3 and by 2, then it is divisible by 6.

(c) Do the same for

If abc is an isosceles right triangle, then it has a 45° interior angle.

14. In the exercises for § 5-10, you were given two formulas defining $\exists_1 x P(x)$, and you proved that the two formulas were logically equivalent.
(a) Write a negation-reduced formula for the negation of each of these defining formulas.
(b) Outline how you would go about proving that the formulas you obtained in (a) are logically equivalent to each other.

15. (a) Using the dictionary below and whatever other standard parts are necessary, write a formula for:

> Any real number is irrational if and only if it cannot be represented by a repeating decimal.

(b) Find an equivalent formula by contraposition.
(c) Translate back into English. (It should make sense.)

Dictionary: N: x is a real number
$ R$: x is rational
$ D$: x can be represented by a repeating decimal

In the remaining exercises, use the following dictionary:

$N(x)$: x is a number
$J(x)$: x is an integer
$G(x, y)$: $x > y$

You may also use positive integral exponents, equality signs, parentheses, and the four arithmetic binary operators, but no radical signs or fractional exponents. For instance, you would represent the statement "The square of every number is positive" by $\forall x[N(x) \Rightarrow G(x^2, 0)]$. For each given statement, you are to
(a) Write a negation in ordinary mathematical language.
(b) Translate the given statement into symbolic form.
(c) Obtain the negation of the formula in negation-reduced form.
(d) Translate your result in (c) back and compare with your version from (a).

16. For any integers x and y such that $x > y$, there is an integer z such that $x > z$ and $z > y$.

17. The square of every negative number is positive.

18. Every positive number has two distinct square roots.

19. $x^n + y^n = z^n$ has no solution in positive integers whenever n is an integer greater than 2.

20. The squares of two distinct positive numbers are distinct.

21. There is a unique positive cube root for any positive number.

Chapter 10

TERMS AND DEFINITIONS

10-1 VARIABLES AS TERMS

We turn now to the question of what sorts of symbols and symbol combinations should be accepted as terms in, for example, an application of the Rule of Instance. Looking back at the discussion of "term" and "variable," as treated on a more intuitive level in § 4-5, it is apparent that any variable should be included among the terms of a system Σ. This suggests that we start a little further back, and try to remove some of the haze around the word "variable."

By a "variable of the system Σ," we mean any symbol that has been so designated. In other words, a variable is any ink shape we choose to so label. As a variable, the shape must be treated as a whole, regardless of what its geography happens to be. In setting up the system Σ, if we say, "Small Latin letters, with or without subscripts or primes, will be used for variables," we have thereby declared x, x_1, and x' to be variables. In using x_1 as a variable, it must not be treated as having two parts, a letter and a numeral, insofar as any logical processes are concerned in that system. Psychologically, we may use subscript notation to help us keep in mind that x_1 and x_2 really have something in common. Logically, as variables, x, x_1, and x' are as different as x, y, and z.

On the other hand, if we have designated only simple letters as variables, we may define and use x_1 or x' in such a way that they would be classified as terms having a free occurrence of the variable x. We did just that in § 8-7 with x^{-1}, and we shall do it again in Chapters 11 and 12 for a set b and its complement b'.

We now start our two-part definition of a term with:

> i. Any variable of Σ is a term, except when used as part of a quantifier, or other specifically excepted location.

An example of another "specifically excepted location" can be found in the set notation $\{x \mid x > y\}$. This is a term, and represents the set of all numbers (for instance) greater than y. The x to the left of the vertical line is like the x in $\forall x$; it is not a term and has the effect of binding just the x in $x > y$. In the term as a whole, x is bound and y is free.

10-2   OTHER TERMS

In approaching the problem of more complex terms, we should keep in mind the intuitive notion that a term is used as a substantive. In a sense, a term should represent something, and it should do so without excessive ambiguity. Our touchstone will be the formula $\exists_1 x P(x)$, to which you were first introduced in the exercises of § 4-8. Later, in Exercises 10 and 11 of § 5-9, it was proved that

$$\exists x [P(x) \wedge \forall y [P(y) \Rightarrow x = y]]$$

and $\quad \exists x \forall y [P(y) \Leftrightarrow x = y]$

were logically equivalent. We shall accept either formula as the written-out version of $\exists_1 x P(x)$. In Exercises 8 and 9 of that section you proved that we can get $P(x)$ from either form [or $P(z)$, and so on], with a use of the Rule of Choice.

We shall want the freedom to invent ad hoc terms in the course of any proof, so the remainder of our two-part definition is framed with respect to a given demonstration.

> ii. Let α represent a symbol or combination of symbols of Σ, with no free occurrence of x. If $A_1, A_2, \ldots, A_n \vdash \exists_1 x [x = \alpha]$, then α is a term with respect to a demonstration of $A_1, A_2, \ldots, A_n \vdash C$. Any variable is free in α if and only if it is free in $\exists_1 x [x = \alpha]$.

Note that in this definition there is no mention of the genesis of α. In general, there are three sources of terms other than pure variables: postulates, substitutive processes, and definitions.

10-3 TERMS BY POSTULATE

In group theory we may be given an undefined operator, say $*$, and the first axiom needed† is the Closure Axiom:

$$\forall yz \exists_1 x [x = y * z]$$

In the Peano axioms for the natural numbers, the basic constructive idea is that of the "successor of z" (the next larger number) frequently denoted by z'. For this we are also given a Closure Axiom:

$$\forall z \exists_1 x [x = z']$$

The statements certifying $x * y$ and z' as terms are easily obtained from these axioms in any demonstration. The presence of the universal quantifiers indicates that y and z are free in the statements within the brackets, and so are free in the respective terms.

We also include among the postulated terms those which are specified as undefined terms, such as "point" in Geometry, or "1" in the Peano system.

EXERCISES

1. Which of the words *line, parallel, plane, angle, altitude, isosceles*, and *polygon* might ordinarily be given as postulated terms in geometry? (Actual practice is somewhat variable.)

2. Which of the words *polynomial, number, ratio, sum* (*of two numbers*), *difference, zero, rational, varies*, and *root* might ordinarily be given as postulated terms in algebra? (Actual practice varies here, too.)

10-4 TERMS BY SUBSTITUTION

We are all accustomed to looking at the use of parentheses in $x - (y + w)$ as a directive concerning the *order* of doing things; *first* the addition,

---

† This would be a more formal approach than we used in § 8-5, where our criteria for terms were still intuitive.

then the subtraction, using the result of the addition. That is probably how we were all taught to interpret parentheses in elementary algebra. For our present needs, we shall look upon the expression as the result of substituting $y + w$ for a variable, say t, in $x - t$. These two binomials are terms, even for completely generalized variables; that is, $\forall yw \exists_1 z[z = y + w]$ and $\forall xt \exists_1 z[z = x - t]$ are provable statements. (Axioms are provable, technically speaking!) We would hope that the result of the substitution described would also be a term.

To state it in more general language, if α represents a term, and if $\varphi(x)$ represents a term with a free occurrence of x, then $\varphi(\alpha)$, the result of substituting α for each free occurrence of x in $\varphi(x)$, should also be a term in the right circumstances. These right circumstances are just those which allow the use of the Rule of Instance.

    i. $\varphi(x)$ must be a term for a generalized x. If we are proving $A_1, A_2, \ldots, A_n \vdash C$, we must be able to show that $A_1, A_2, \ldots, A_n \vdash \forall x \exists_1 z[z = \varphi(x)]$.

    ii. We must be able to show that $A_1, A_2, \ldots, A_n \vdash \exists_1 z[z = \alpha]$, that is, that α is a term.

    iii. $z = \varphi(x)$ and $z = \varphi(\alpha)$ must form a $P(x)$—$P(\alpha)$ pair, satisfying the restriction that no variable occurring free in α becomes bound by the substitution of α for x.

If these three conditions are met, we can get $\exists_1 z[z = \varphi(\alpha)]$ by applying the Rule of Instance to the statement $\forall x \exists_1 z[z = \varphi(x)]$.†

In the example of $x - (y + w)$, what we actually substituted for t was not $y + w$, but $(y + w)$. The necessity for association symbols like parentheses arises most commonly out of the $\varphi(x)$—$\varphi(\alpha)$ process of substitution. The use of parentheses can be formalized, or, alternatively, we can simply accept the identity of (α) and α whenever α is a term, by notational agreement.

10-5 TERMS BY DEFINITION

The process of substitution can lead to rather complicated expressions. For example, we could easily arrive at a statement like

$$(1) \quad \exists_1 z \left[z = (x + y) \frac{\sin x}{\cos y} \right]$$

---

† We are assuming that z does not occur free in $\varphi(\alpha)$, nor, a fortiori, in $\varphi(x)$.

We might be satisfied to apply the Rule of Choice and whatever else is needed at this point to get

$$(2) \quad z = (x + y)\frac{\sin x}{\cos y}$$

and to use z as a more convenient handle than the longer expression.

On the other hand, we might want to retain the identity of the free variables x and y, perhaps with an eye to future substitutions for these variables. We may then adopt some novel symbol—that is, novel to the particular proof in which we are at that moment engaged. $F(x, y)$, $x \circ y$, $\langle x, y \rangle$ are some typical possibilities. For maximum usefulness, what we need is an equality, which we will be able to use with Equality Substitution, for example,

$$(3) \quad F(x, y) = (x + y)\frac{\sin x}{\cos y}$$

We can then apply (3) to (1), and obtain

$$(4) \quad \exists_1 z[z = F(x, y)]$$

thereby establishing $F(x, y)$ as a term. However, this would not allow the use of $F(17, y)$ as a term, unless we can generalize (4), or unless (1) can be stated in more general terms. As it happens, if the latter can be asserted in the real numbers, so can

$$(5) \quad \forall x \exists_1 z\left[z = (x + y)\frac{\sin x}{\cos y} \right]$$

This would suggest a similarly strengthened definition:

$$(6) \quad \forall x\left[F(x, y) = (x + y)\frac{\sin x}{\cos y} \right]$$

Indeed, unless we have the generalized definition, we cannot substitute in (5) to get the generalized version of (4)

$$(7) \quad \forall x \exists_1 z[z = F(x, y)]$$

which we need to establish $F(17, y)$ as a term. The question of generalizing with respect to y will be discussed in § 10-8.

Although it is true that definitions like (3) or (6) are merely matters of convenience, they also fit into more general situations in which a definition is more than a permit to substitute one formula for another. Let us consider a standard set of axioms for the real numbers. After 0 has been established as a term, we find the axiom:

$$(8) \quad \forall x \exists_1 y [x + y = 0]$$

According to this axiom, for each number x there is a unique number y with a very special property relative to x. We usually denote that number by $-x$. Any number will have that special property if and only if it is the unique one which the new term represents. The definition of $-x$ therefore takes the following form:

$$(9) \quad \forall xy [y = -x \Leftrightarrow x + y = 0]$$

Speaking more generally, suppose we have obtained, in the course of a proof that $A_1, A_2, \ldots, A_n \vdash C$, the statement

$$(10) \quad \forall y_1 y_2 \cdots y_m \exists_1 z P(z)$$

where $P(z)$ is a statement containing free occurrences of the variables y_1 to y_m, z, and possibly others. Then, taking a novel formula α that explicitly mentions all the free variables of $P(z)$, *except* z, we define that formula with

$$(11) \quad \forall y_1 y_2 \cdots y_m \forall z [z = \alpha \Leftrightarrow P(z)]$$

The Rule of Substitution for Biconditionals then gives us

$$(12) \quad \forall y_1 y_2 \cdots y_m \exists_1 z [z = \alpha]$$

To see that the first type of definition can be subsumed under (10) and (11), take $z = (x + y) \sin x / \cos y$ as the $P(z)$ of (10), and let x be the y_1 of that formula, with $m = 1$. This gives us (5). With $F(x, y)$ for the α in (11), we get

$$(13) \quad \forall x \forall z \left[z = F(x, y) \Leftrightarrow z = (x + y) \frac{\sin x}{\cos y} \right]$$

We can now obtain (7) by using Biconditional Substitution (see Exercise 2).

EXERCISES

1. What is needed besides the Rule of Choice to get (2) from (1)?

2. Prove that (5), (13) $\vdash$ (7).

3. Prove that (7), (13) $\vdash$ (6).

10-6 CONSTANTS

When $\exists_1 z P(z)$ has no free variables, the corresponding definition will give us a "constant." There are no special rules for a constant; its definition does all that is needed. One does have to keep in mind that a constant is not a variable, particularly when custom has established a symbol that might cause confusion, as in the use of π and e for certain irrational numbers.

Strictly speaking, in accordance with the first definition in § 4-6, terms like "$1 + 1$" or even "-1" would not be classed as constants, since they are not primitive symbols, but formed by substitutive processes. Of course, having proved or postulated that $\forall xy \exists_1 z[z = x + y]$, we can easily get $\exists_1 z[z = 1 + 1]$. We may then define the constant "2."

We could maintain this distinction by using "constant term" as a more general expression which would include constants. That is, if $\exists_1 z[z = \alpha]$ is provable, and has no free variables, then α may be called a "constant term." However, no harm is done by extending the use of "constant" to include such terms. Note that an expression like $x - x$ still may not be called a constant, since it has free variables.

10-7 DEFINING NEW STATEMENT FORMS

In addition to defining terms, we may sometimes define new forms for statements. These definitions are strictly for convenience, and can be presented at the symbol level, as we did with the biconditional operator. For example, in Chapter 11, we shall define $a \subseteq b$ by

$$a \subseteq b \quad \text{for} \quad \forall x[x \in a \Leftrightarrow x \in b]$$

In Chapter 12, we shall define $a \subseteq b$ all over again by

$$a \subseteq b \quad \text{for} \quad a \cup b = b$$

In each case, the form at the left is a more convenient way of writing the expression on the right, which has at that point already been established as in legitimate form for a statement of the system.

Occurrence of free variables should correspond exactly in the two versions, but bound variables in the old formula can be omitted from the new one, as with the x in the first definition of $a \subseteq b$ above.

Alternatively, one could define a new statement form by using a biconditional. Thus the definition of $a \subseteq b$ in Chapter 11 could be given by

Definition

$$a \subseteq b: \quad \forall ab [a \subseteq b \Leftrightarrow \forall x[x \in a \Leftrightarrow x \in b]]$$

Notice the use of overall quantifiers here. This kind of definition for a statement would be part of the formal basis, just as the formal definitions of terms of § 10-5.

EXERCISE

Two ways of defining $a \subseteq b$ for Chapter 11 were given above.
(a) Show that if we permit the free substitution authorized by the first definition, then we can obtain the statement given as the second definition.
(b) Show that taking the second definition as a basic assumption will make possible the same kind of free substitution that the first definition allows.

10-8 DEFINITIONS AND THE DEMONSTRATION

Just where does a definition of a term fit into our rules? As suggested in §§ 1-6 and 8-5, it is to be considered a primary assumption, that is, one of the A_i's in any demonstration in which it is used. It can be dangerous to throw in a new assumption in the middle of a demonstration, even for mere convenience; if it contains a free variable, its presence may invalidate a previous use of Choice or Generalization. The obvious thing to do is to see that your definition has no free variables. This is not simply a matter of tacking on universal quantifiers, for, looking back at the discussion around the definition of $F(x, y)$ in § 10-5, we can see that it would be a questionable procedure to prefix $\forall y$ to (6) to get $\forall y x [F(x, y) = (x + y) \sin x / \cos y]$, since the corresponding existential statement $\forall y x \exists_1 z [z = (x + y) \sin x / \cos y]$ is false. (Notice that $y = \pi/2$ furnishes a counterexample.)

On the other hand, since our discussion is presumed to have taken place within a context where (5) has been legitimately stated, there must have been an assumption or previous statement from which we could establish that $\cos y$ could not be zero. Let us suppose that there was a previous statement $|y| < \pi/2$. It does not matter whether the origin of this specialized free variable was an assumption or a use of the Rule of Choice. We can prove

$$\forall y \left[|y| < \frac{\pi}{2} \Rightarrow \forall x \exists_1 z \left[z = (x + y) \frac{\sin x}{\cos y} \right] \right]$$

so we simply incorporate the restriction into a conditional definition:

$$\forall y \left[|y| < \frac{\pi}{2} \Rightarrow \forall x \left[F(x, y) = (x + y) \frac{\sin x}{\cos y} \right] \right]$$

or, in the more general format,

$$\forall y \left[|y| < \frac{\pi}{2} \Rightarrow \forall x \forall z \left[z = F(x, y) \Leftrightarrow z = (x + y) \frac{\sin x}{\cos y} \right] \right]$$

This definition may be assumed without interfering in any way with the logical processes of a demonstration.

10-9 MORE FORMAL VERSIONS OF FOUR BASIC RULES

Now that we have a formal basis for judging whether or not α is a term, we can revise the Rules of Instance, Example, Equality Substitution, and Reflexivity of Equality so that the role of intuition is still further reduced. We begin by redefining $P(x)$—$P(\alpha)$ pairs for a given system Σ. $P(x)$—$P(\alpha)$ will represent a pair of statements with the following properties:

(a) x is a variable; α represents a symbol or combination of symbols of Σ.

(b) $P(\alpha)$ can be obtained by substituting α for every free occurrence of x.

The definitions of $P(x)$—$P(y)$ and $P(\alpha)$—$P(\beta)$ pairs need no revision.

In order not to interfere with the proof of the Deduction Theorem, the revised Rule of Instance would take the form:

Instance: S_i has the form $\exists_1 z[z = \alpha] \Rightarrow [\forall x P(x) \Rightarrow P(\alpha)]$ provided that no variable occurring free in α becomes bound by the substitution of α for x in the $P(x)$—$P(\alpha)$ pair.

To be able to get statements having the form of the Instance rule as originally given, we need only to establish that $\exists_1 z[z = \alpha]$. In other words, whenever α is a term, then the old rule holds. In the next two chapters we shall continue to refer to the original form and its derivatives in Chapter 7 as the Rule of Instance, but we shall take care that $\exists_1 z[z = \alpha]$ is available, even if we do not use it explicitly in the less formal proofs.

EXERCISE

State revised versions of the other rules mentioned in this section.

10-10 A THEOREM ON EQUALITY

As an outgrowth of § 10-4, we can add a bonus to this chapter in the form of a universal theorem.

Among the axioms of Euclid, there is one that is traditionally translated: If equals be added to equals, then the wholes are equal. Whatever this means in geometry (are congruent angles "equal"?), in an algebraic setting it can be precisely stated:

$$\forall xyzw[x = y \wedge z = w \Rightarrow x + z = y + w]$$

In any system that allows the form $x + y$ as a term, the statement above is provable, and need not be taken as axiomatic (see Exercises 2 and 3). More generally:

UT 19: With α, β, $\varphi(\alpha)$, $\varphi(\beta)$ as described in § 10-4,

$$\forall Z[\alpha = \beta \Rightarrow \varphi(\alpha) = \varphi(\beta)]$$

In § 7-4 we extended the $P(x)$—$P(\alpha)$ notation to n variables and n α's. We were then able to extend the Rules of Instance and Example correspondingly. In similar fashion, we can extend the $\varphi(x)$—$\varphi(\alpha)$ notation to n variables and α's. UT 19 can then be stated as follows:

UT 19: $\forall Z[\alpha_1 = \beta_1 \wedge \alpha_2 = \beta_2 \wedge \cdots \wedge \alpha_n = \beta_n \Rightarrow$

$$\varphi(\alpha_1, \alpha_2, \ldots, \alpha_n) = \varphi(\beta_1, \beta_2, \ldots, \beta_n)]$$

The algebraic rule for adding equalities can now be seen as an instance of this extended UT 19, with $n = 2$.

EXERCISES

1. Prove UT 19 (first form). Use Equality Substitution, with $P(\alpha)$ being $\varphi(\alpha) = \varphi(\alpha)$.

2. Assuming closure for $+$ (that is, $\alpha + \beta$ is a term whenever α and β are), prove:
$$\forall xyzw[x = y \wedge z = w \Rightarrow x + z = y + w]$$

using UT 19 in its unextended form. You may use the metatheorem proved in Exercise 2 of § 6-4, if it will help.

3. Find three examples of mathematical theorems or axioms, other than that given in Exercises 2, which are merely instances of simple applications of UT 19, and prove one of them.

Chapter 11

THE SYSTEM {͞x, ∈}

11-1 INTRODUCTION

In this chapter the content of Chapters 2 through 10 will be applied to a structure which is probably known to you on an informal and intuitive level. We shall develop an abstract system competent to deal with the simpler relations among the subsets of a given universe. The purpose is threefold— first, to illustrate how a system can be set up in harmony with the rules, second, to give you some practice in formal proof, and, third, to lay bare the parallel between relations among sets and tautological formulas.

The system originates in set theory, but we shall present it in even more abstract terms. Instead of "element," as used in set theory, we shall use "first-category term." Instead of "set," we shall use "second-category term." The category of a term will be determined on a formal basis. The set-theoretic model will be referred to as the "standard" one, and in the exercises at the end of the chapter you will find other interpretations. No harm will be done if you think of first-category terms as representing elements of a given set, and second-category terms as representing subsets of that set, while you study the system.

In describing $P(x)$—$P(\alpha)$ pairs in § 4-9, the following restriction was included:

> (b) If the variable represents an element of a restricted class by
> notational convention, then the term α must represent an
> element of that class.

With respect to the present system, this restriction requires that in applying, for example, the Rule of Instance, the α involved must belong to the same category as the variable it replaces. However, the criteria for the construction of statements will take care of this, in that when α and x are of different categories, then $P(x)$ and $P(\alpha)$ will not both be statements.

11-2 UNDEFINED EXPRESSIONS

      (i) Variables of the first category: x, y, z.
          Variables of the second category: a, b, c, d.
     (ii) Sentential operators, brackets, ∃.
    (iii) =, ∈.

The last two symbols, of which only the second is new, denote the two basic relations that will concern us in this chapter. Grammatically, they function as verbs, in the formation of atomic statements. We have a good English word, "equals," for one of these, but to verbalize the other we must use phrases such as "belongs to," or "is an element of." This is purely accidental; there is no linguistic reason why the English language should not have a single word for this relationship. German comes close with "zugehören." Even though "⅄" appears in the name of the system, it will be defined. In the standard interpretation, ⅄ is often called the "universal set." Parentheses will have their usual grouping function for terms.

11-3 CRITERIA FOR STATEMENTS

    (1) _____ ∈ _____ is a statement, when the left blank is replaced by a term of the first category, and the right blank by a term of the second category.
    (2) _____ = _____ is a statement when both blanks are replaced by terms of the same category.
    (3) ∃_____[_____] is a statement if the left blank is replaced by a variable of either category, and the right blank is replaced by a statement.
    (4) [_____]

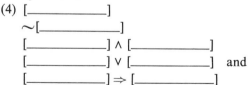

are each statements if the blanks are replaced by statements.
    (5) Additional statement forms may be defined by giving permission to substitute a novel combination of symbols for a

combination that already meets the criteria for a statement. The new form must exhibit as free variables all those and only those that occur free in the old form.

(6) For any combination of symbols to qualify as a statement, it must be constructible by a finite number of applications of the constructions (1) through (5).

The forms $\_ \Leftrightarrow \_$ and $\forall \_$ have been defined in §§ 2-6 and 4-1, and we shall use these without repeating their definitions. For $\exists_1$ we shall choose the second form given in § 5-9,

$$\exists_1 x P(x) \quad \text{for} \quad \exists x \forall y [P(y) \Leftrightarrow x = y]$$

We shall relax the rules given above for constructing statements just far enough to allow the scope conventions of §§ 2-7 and 4-1.

EXERCISES

For each of the following formulas, state whether it qualifies as a statement of $\{ \ell, \in \}$ at this point. If your answer is negative, give reasons.

1. $\exists a \forall x [x \in b \wedge x \in a]$

2. $\sim \exists x [b \in x \Rightarrow a \in x]$

3. $\forall ab [a \subseteq b \Rightarrow b = a]$

4. $\exists x \forall y [\exists a [x \in a] \Rightarrow \exists b [y \in b]]$

5. $\forall mn [m = n \Rightarrow \forall y [x \in m \Rightarrow x \in n]]$

6. $\forall ab [a \Leftrightarrow b \Rightarrow \forall y [x \in b \Rightarrow x \in a]]$

7. $\exists ax [\forall b [x \in b] \Leftrightarrow \sim a]$

8. $\forall ab [a = b \Rightarrow \forall x [x \in a \Leftrightarrow x \in b]]$

9. $\forall x [P(x) \Rightarrow \exists a [x \in a]]$

11-4 AXIOMS AND DEFINITIONS

All our axioms fall into the following single pattern or "scheme."

> **Axiom Scheme:** If P is a statement with no free occurrence of the variable a, then
>
> $$\forall Z \exists_1 a \forall x [x \in a \Leftrightarrow P]$$
>
> is an axiom. In this scheme, x and a are only representative, and may be replaced by any other first- and second-category variables, respectively.

This gives us an unlimited set of axioms, but we shall make use of only six.

> **Axiom 1:** $\exists_1 a \forall x [x \in a \Leftrightarrow x = x]$
>
> **Axiom 2:** $\forall b \exists_1 a \forall x [x \in a \Leftrightarrow \sim [x \in b]]$
>
> **Axiom 3:** $\forall y \exists_1 a \forall x [x \in a \Leftrightarrow x = y]$
>
> **Axiom 4:** $\forall bc \exists_1 a \forall x [x \in a \Leftrightarrow [x \in b \wedge x \in c]]$
>
> **Axiom 5:** $\forall bc \exists_1 a \forall x [x \in a \Leftrightarrow [x \in b \vee x \in c]]$
>
> **Axiom 6:** $\forall b \exists_1 a \forall x [x \in a \Leftrightarrow x \in b]$

To help you fix these axioms in your mind, it would be a good idea to translate them into the language of sets, if you have not already done so as you were reading them.

Axioms 1 through 5 each suggest a definition for a second-category term—constant in the case of Axiom 1, with one free variable in the case of Axioms 2 and 3, and with two free variables in the case of Axioms 4 and 5. We shall make particular use of the following four definitions:

Definitions

$$\maltese: \quad \forall a [a = \maltese \Leftrightarrow \forall x [x \in a \Leftrightarrow x = x]]$$
$$b': \quad \forall ab [a = b' \Leftrightarrow \forall x [x \in a \Leftrightarrow \sim [x \in b]]]$$
$$b \cap c: \quad \forall abc [a = b \cap c \Leftrightarrow \forall x [x \in a \Leftrightarrow [x \in b] \wedge [x \in c]]]$$
$$b \cup c: \quad \forall abc [a = b \cup c \Leftrightarrow \forall x [x \in a \Leftrightarrow [x \in b] \vee [x \in c]]]$$

We also define some convenient statement forms.

Definitions

$$\alpha \subseteq \beta \quad \text{for} \quad \forall x[x \in \alpha \Rightarrow x \in \beta]$$
$$\alpha \notin \beta \quad \text{for} \quad \sim[\alpha \in \beta]$$
$$\alpha \neq \beta \quad \text{for} \quad \sim[\alpha = \beta]$$
$$\alpha \nsubseteq \beta \quad \text{for} \quad \sim[\alpha \subseteq \beta]$$

In the last four definitions, the α and β must be of the correct categories to make the formula on the right a statement under our rules. In the standard interpretation, b' is called the **complement of** b, $b \cap c$ is called the **intersection of** b **and** c, and $b \cup c$ is called the **union of** b **and** c. They can also be verbalized as b *prime*, b *cap* c, and b *cup* c, respectively. To help you remember the definitions of cap and cup, observe the resemblance (not accidental) of $\cap$ to $\wedge$, and of $\cup$ to $\vee$. The statement form $\alpha \subseteq \beta$ can be read α *is a subset of* β, or α *is contained in* β.

Since $\cap$ and $\cup$ are used between terms to build other terms, they will have smaller scope than $=$, $\in$, or $\subseteq$, which build statements. In turn, $=$, $\in$, and $\subseteq$ have smaller scope than a sentential operator, since they form atomic statements.

EXERCISE

The Russell Antinomy: Let us consider the axiom obtained by using $P : x \notin x$ in the axiom scheme.

Axiom: $\exists_1 a \forall x[x \in a \Leftrightarrow x \notin x]$

This seems to be a reasonable sort of set—the one characterized by the fact that no element is a member of itself. We now use it to prove an interesting theorem.

1. $\exists_1 a \forall x[x \in a \Leftrightarrow x \notin x]$ Ax

2. $\exists a \forall b[\forall x[x \in b \Leftrightarrow x \notin x] \Leftrightarrow b = a]$ Def $\exists_1 a P(a)$

3. $\forall b[\forall x[x \in b \Leftrightarrow x \notin x] \Leftrightarrow b = a]$

4. $\forall x[x \in a \Leftrightarrow x \notin x] \Leftrightarrow a = a$

5. $a = a$

6. $\forall x[x \in a \Leftrightarrow x \notin x]$

7. $a \in a \Leftrightarrow a \notin a$

8. $a \in a \wedge a \notin a$ Tau Inf S_7

9. $\exists a[a \in a \wedge a \notin a]$

Think about the entity whose existence you have just proved. Can you see how objectionable it is? Is there a flaw in the system, or has a regulation been disobeyed?

11-5 SOME SIMPLE, BASIC THEOREMS

Before we begin discussing the theorems, let us consider the form our proofs will take in this chapter. With some minor additional relaxations, they will be formal proofs as defined in § 8-4. In a formal proof of a theorem, you are allowed to use postulates, definitions of terms, previously proved theorems, and instances of universal theorems without specifically listing them as assumptions, even though the justification for such a step does involve the Rule of Assumption. Instead of writing "As" in the justification column, we shall write Th 1a, Def b′, UT 10, and so on. We shall relax our rules to allow discreet changes of (bound) variables in the statements themselves, as sanctioned by UT 8 and UT 9. Thus, in the proof of Lemma B for Theorem 3 below, the first step will be

$$\forall b \exists_1 c \forall x [x \in c \Leftrightarrow x \in b] \qquad \qquad \| \text{Ax } 6$$

where c has replaced a in the actual statement of the theorem. Step 2 in the exercise of the preceding section shows how we shall handle "convenience" definitions of statement forms.

The six theorems grouped under Theorem 1 have the function of establishing the legitimacy of using certain expressions as terms, as promised in § 10-9. The proofs are quite trivial, and have been left for exercises.

>**Theorem 1a:** $\exists_1 a [a = \maltese]$
>   **1b:** $\forall b \exists_1 a [a = b']$
>   **1c:** $\forall bc \exists_1 a [a = b \cap c]$
>   **1d:** $\forall bc \exists_1 a [a = b \cup c]$
>   **1e:** $\exists_1 a [a = \maltese']$

Theorem 1a permits the use of the constant $\maltese$ as a term. Theorem 1b permits the use of α' as a term, for any second-category term α, because it is generalized on the second-category variable b. Theorems 1c and 1d permit $\alpha \cap \beta$ and $\alpha \cup \beta$, whenever α and β are second-category terms. Theorem 1e establishes the existence of another constant to which we give an unnecessary but customary label (unnecessary because we could always use $\maltese'$).

Definition

$$\varnothing: \quad \varnothing = \mathcal{1}'$$

This is a definition of the first sort mentioned in § 10-5, and illustrated there by (3). Having no free variables, it requires no quantification. From it we get

Theorem 1f: $\exists_1 a[a = \varnothing]$

The five parts of Theorem 2 state the basic properties of the five terms we have defined. These theorems form the connecting link between the theorems on subsets which start at Theorem 5, and the sentential calculus of Chapter 3.

Theorem 2a: $\forall ax[x \in a' \Leftrightarrow x \notin a]$
      2b: $\forall x[x \in \mathcal{1}]$
      2c: $\forall x[x \notin \varnothing]$
      2d: $\forall abx[x \in a \cap b \Leftrightarrow x \in a \wedge x \in b]$
      2e: $\forall abx[x \in a \cup b \Leftrightarrow x \in a \vee x \in b]$

Each part of Theorem 2 is proved by using the corresponding definition. For example, by applying the Rule of Instance to the definition of b', with $a \to a'$ and $b \to a$, we get

$$a' = a' \Leftrightarrow \forall x[x \in a' \Leftrightarrow x \notin a]$$

from which 2a is easily derived.

If we read Theorems 2b and 2c using the standard interpretation, we can see why $\mathcal{1}$ is called the "universal" set and $\varnothing$ is called the "empty" set.

EXERCISES

1. Show that, in the standard interpretation, the set $\mathcal{1}$ is not empty, by stating and proving a suitable theorem.
(*Hint for Exercises 2 through 6:* Match a definition with an axiom.)

2. Prove Theorem 1a.

3. Prove Theorem 1b.

4. Prove Theorem 1c.

5. Prove Theorem 1d.

6. Prove Theorem 1e.

7. Prove Theorem 2a.

8. Prove Theorem 2b.

9. Prove Theorem 2c.

10. Prove Theorem 2d.

11. Prove Theorem 2e.

11-6 MEMBERSHIP AND EQUALITY

The next two theorems connect membership with equality (in the standard interpretation). Theorem 3 concerns equality of sets, and could be paraphrased, "A set is completely determined by the elements in it." Theorem 4 concerns equality of elements and could be paraphrased, "An element is completely determined by the sets it is in."

Theorem 3: $\forall ab[a = b \Leftrightarrow \forall x[x \in a \Leftrightarrow x \in b]]$

We shall use two lemmas, and shall leave the justifications as an exercise.

Lemma A: $a = b \vdash \forall x[x \in a \Leftrightarrow x \in b]$

Proof

1. $a = b$
2. $\forall x[x \in a \Leftrightarrow x \in a]$
3. $\forall x[x \in a \Leftrightarrow x \in b]$

Lemma B: $\forall x[x \in a \Leftrightarrow x \in b] \vdash a = b$

It was for this lemma that Axiom 6 was chosen.

Proof

1. $\forall b \exists_1 c \forall x[x \in c \Leftrightarrow x \in b]$ ‖ Ax 6

2. $\forall b \exists c \forall a[\forall x[x \in a \Leftrightarrow x \in b] \Leftrightarrow a = c]$ ‖ Def $\exists_1 c P(c)$

3. $\exists c \forall a[\forall x[x \in a \Leftrightarrow x \in b] \Leftrightarrow a = c]$

4. $\forall a[\forall x[x \in a \Leftrightarrow x \in b] \Leftrightarrow a = c]$

5. $\forall x[x \in a \Leftrightarrow x \in b] \Leftrightarrow a = c$

We are now in a position to make use of the assumption.

6. $\forall x[x \in a \Leftrightarrow x \in b]$

7. $a = c$

If we can show that $b = c$, we can get $a = b$ by substitution. Looking at S_4, we see how to do this.

8. $\forall x[x \in b \Leftrightarrow x \in b] \Leftrightarrow b = c$

9. $\forall x[x \in b \Leftrightarrow x \in b]$

10. $b = c$

11. $a = b$

With the Biconditional Theorem, these two lemmas prove:

$$\vdash a = b \Leftrightarrow \forall x[x \in a \Leftrightarrow x \in b]$$

Two steps of Generalization now give us the theorem.

> **Corollary:** $\forall ab[a = b \Leftrightarrow [a \subseteq b] \wedge [b \subseteq a]]$

> **Theorem 4:** $\forall xy[x = y \Leftrightarrow \forall a[x \in a \Leftrightarrow y \in a]]$

Proof: Exercise 4.

EXERCISES

1. (a) Prove: $\forall ab[a \neq b \Leftrightarrow \exists x[x \in a \wedge x \notin b] \vee \exists x[x \notin a \wedge x \in b]]$
(b) State the content of this theorem colloquially, using the standard interpretation.

2. Using the theorem of Exercise 1, prove $\mathbf{1} \neq \varnothing$.

3. Furnish the justifications in the proofs of Lemmas A and B of Theorem 3.

4. Prove Theorem 4. As in the proof of Theorem 3, split the proof into two lemmas, and use the Biconditional Theorem. The proof of the first lemma will be almost identical with that of Lemma A. The second lemma has a proof much like that of Lemma B, but instead of Axiom 6 you should start with Axiom 3, in the following form:

$$\forall y \exists a \forall b [\forall x [x \in b \Leftrightarrow x = y] \Leftrightarrow a = b]$$

Be careful to select the right α when removing $\forall b$ from this, and don't forget to use the assumption.

5. Prove the Corollary of Theorem 3. Using the definition of the biconditional and UT 10 will make this easy.

11-7 SUBSET THEOREMS AND TAUTOLOGIES

The remaining theorems involve only second-category terms, and overall universal quantifiers. As you shall see, each may be proved fairly efficiently without using any previous theorems other than Theorems 2 and 3 as assumptions. The approach is quite systematic—each theorem is referred back to a tautology that is completely spelled out by the theorem itself.

The order of the remaining theorems is therefore of no logical significance. In Chapter 12 a different approach to the same theorems is used, wherein order matters much more. The list below follows substantially the order used in Chapter 12.

Theorem 5: $\forall ab[a \cap b = \varnothing \wedge a \cup b = \star \Leftrightarrow a = b']$
    6a: $\forall a[a \cup a' = \star]$
    6b: $\forall a[a \cap a' = \varnothing]$
    7a: $\forall ab[a \cup b = b \cup a]$
    7b: $\forall ab[a \cap b = b \cap a]$
    8a: $\forall abc[a \cup (b \cap c) = (a \cup b) \cap (a \cup c)]$
    8b: $\forall abc[a \cap (b \cup c) = (a \cap b) \cup (a \cap c)]$
    9a: $\forall ab[(a \cup b) \cap (a \cup b') = a]$
    9b: $\forall ab[(a \cap b) \cup (a \cap b') = a]$
    10a: $\forall a[a \cup a = a]$
    10b: $\forall a[a \cap a = a]$
    11: $\forall ab[a \cup b = a \Leftrightarrow a \cap b = b]$
    12a: $\forall ab[a \subseteq b \Leftrightarrow a \cup b = b]$

12b: $\forall ab[b \subseteq a \Leftrightarrow a \cap b = b]$

  13: $\forall abc[a \subseteq b \wedge b \subseteq c \Rightarrow a \subseteq c]$

14a: $\forall a[a \subseteq \mathbf{1}]$.

14b: $\forall a[\varnothing \subseteq a]$

15a: $\forall a[a \cap \mathbf{1} = a]$

15b: $\forall a[a \cup \varnothing = a]$

16a: $\forall a[a \cup \mathbf{1} = \mathbf{1}]$

16b: $\forall a[a \cap \varnothing = \varnothing]$

17a: $\forall ab[a \subseteq a \cup b]$

17b: $\forall ab[a \cap b \subseteq a]$

18a: $\forall abc[a \subseteq b \Rightarrow a \cup c \subseteq b \cup c]$

18b: $\forall abc[b \subseteq a \Rightarrow b \cap c \subseteq a \cap c]$

19a: $\forall abcd[a \subseteq b \wedge c \subseteq d \Rightarrow a \cup c \subseteq b \cup d]$

19b: $\forall abcd[b \subseteq a \wedge d \subseteq c \Rightarrow b \cap d \subseteq a \cap c]$

20a: $\forall abc[a \subseteq c \wedge b \subseteq c \Leftrightarrow a \cup b \subseteq c]$

20b: $\forall abc[c \subseteq a \wedge c \subseteq b \Leftrightarrow c \subseteq a \cap b]$

21a: $\forall abc[a \cup (b \cup c) = (a \cup b) \cup c]$

21b: $\forall abc[a \cap (b \cap c) = (a \cap b) \cap c]$

  22: $\forall a[a = (a')']$

  23: $\forall ab[a' = b' \Leftrightarrow a = b]$

24a: $\forall ab[(a \cup b)' = a' \cap b']$

24b: $\forall ab[(a \cap b)' = a' \cup b']$

  25: $\forall ab[a \subseteq b \Leftrightarrow b' \subseteq a']$

26a: $\forall ab[a = b' \Leftrightarrow a \cup b = a' \cup b']$

26b: $\forall ab[a = b' \Leftrightarrow a \cap b = a' \cap b']$

27a: $\forall ab[a \cup b = \mathbf{1} \Leftrightarrow b' \subseteq a]$

27b: $\forall ab[a \cap b = \varnothing \Leftrightarrow a \subseteq b']$

To construct the appropriate tautology for a given second-category theorem from this list, we replace each term in the theorem by a statement, in the following way:

1. Replace constants and variables $\mathbf{1}$, $\varnothing$, a, b, ... , by $x \in \mathbf{1}$, $x \in \varnothing$, $x \in a$, $x \in b$, ... , respectively.

2. Replace

    $\cap$ with $\wedge$

    $\cup$ with $\vee$

    $\subseteq$ with $\Rightarrow$

    $=$ with $\Leftrightarrow$

(It may be necessary to add brackets at this point.)

3. If any term had a prime attached, negate the corresponding statement, and remove the prime.

4. All existing sentential operators are left unchanged, but overall quantifiers are dropped.

Let Q be the statement resulting from this construction. Then

$$x \in \maltese \Rightarrow x \notin \varnothing \Rightarrow Q$$

is a tautology, if the theorem is valid. If either $\maltese$ or $\varnothing$ is not mentioned in the theorem, the corresponding substatement can be dropped from the above formula, and it will still be a tautology.

We may put this in the form of a metatheorem, which we shall not attempt to prove:

> Let P be any statement using only second-category terms, with no bound variables. Let Q be the statement formed from P according to the directions above. Then $\forall ZP$ is provable if and only if Q is tautological.

Since we shall not prove this metatheorem, proofs of the theorems on the list must be given without invoking it. This does not mean that we may not use the prescription for constructing the related tautology as a starting point for each proof.

EXERCISE

Without looking at the explanation in Chapter 12, see if you can discover the relation between the "a" and "b" theorems in the above list. What can you say about the theorems that do not have "a" and "b" versions?

11-8 ILLUSTRATIVE PROOFS

As we remarked in the preceding section, the order in which the second-category theorems are proved is immaterial. Our first example will be Theorem 8b, and you may observe that no theorem after Theorem 3 will be used in its proof.

Theorem 8b: $\forall abc[a \cap (b \cup c) = (a \cap b) \cup (a \cap c)]$

Proof: We start with the tautology prescribed in the preceding section.

1. $x \in a \wedge [x \in b \vee x \in c] \Leftrightarrow$
   $[x \in a \wedge x \in b] \vee [x \in a \wedge x \in c]$

We have to work back from this to the theorem. To do this, we work with those parts of Theorem 2 that deal with cups and caps.

2. $\forall abx[x \in a \cap b \Leftrightarrow x \in a \wedge x \in b]$

3. $\forall abx[x \in a \cup b \Leftrightarrow x \in a \vee x \in b]$

Now we play an aria con variazioni on S_2 and S_3, using Instance.

4. $x \in a \cap b \Leftrightarrow x \in a \wedge x \in b$

5. $x \in a \cap c \Leftrightarrow x \in a \wedge x \in c$

6. $x \in b \cup c \Leftrightarrow x \in b \vee x \in c$

7. $x \in a \cap (b \cup c) \Leftrightarrow x \in a \wedge x \in b \cup c$

8. $x \in (a \cap b) \cup (a \cap c) \Leftrightarrow$
   $x \in a \cap b \vee x \in a \cap c$

We can now eliminate the sentential operators $\wedge$ and $\vee$ in S_1, one by one, by using Biconditional Substitution with S_4 through S_8. Five such replacements end with

13. $x \in a \cap (b \cup c) \Leftrightarrow x \in (a \cap b) \cup (a \cap c)$

14. $\forall x[x \in a \cap (b \cup c) \Leftrightarrow$
    $x \in (a \cap b) \cup (a \cap c)]$

Our next move is to replace the biconditional statement in S_{14} with a statement about equality of sets. Theorem 3 is relevant here.

15. $\forall ab[a = b \Leftrightarrow \forall x[x \in a \Leftrightarrow x \in b]]$

16. $a \cap (b \cup c) = (a \cap b) \cup (a \cap c) \Leftrightarrow S_{14}$ Instance

17. $a \cap (b \cup c) = (a \cap b) \cup (a \cap c)$

Since the only previously specified variable does not occur in S_{17}, we may use Generalization.

20. $\forall abc[a \cap (b \cup c) = (a \cap b) \cup (a \cap c)]$ ‖

The next proof uses a full-length tautology and all five parts of Theorem 2.

Theorem 5: $\forall ab[a \cap b = \varnothing \wedge a \cup b = \mathcal{1} \Leftrightarrow a = b']$

Proof

1. $x \in \mathcal{1} \Rightarrow x \notin \varnothing \Rightarrow [[x \in a \wedge x \in b \Leftrightarrow$
   $x \in \varnothing] \wedge [x \in a \vee x \in b \Leftrightarrow x \in \mathcal{1}] \Leftrightarrow$
   $[x \in a \Leftrightarrow x \notin b]]$
2. $\forall ax[x \in a' \Leftrightarrow x \notin a]$
3. $\forall x[x \in \mathcal{1}]$
4. $\forall x[x \notin \varnothing]$
5. $\forall abx[x \in a \cap b \Leftrightarrow x \in a \wedge x \in b]$
6. $\forall abx[x \in a \cup b \Leftrightarrow x \in a \vee x \in b]$
7. $x \in \mathcal{1}$
8. $x \notin \varnothing$
9. $[x \in a \wedge x \in b \Leftrightarrow x \in \varnothing] \wedge$
   $[x \in a \vee x \in b \Leftrightarrow x \in \mathcal{1}] \Leftrightarrow$
   $[x \in a \Leftrightarrow x \notin b]$

S_9 is not really necessary, but it replaces S_1 by something closer to the theorem to be proved. We shall use steps 2, 5, and 6 on S_9. This time we do not need to use Instance on S_5 and S_6, since the variables are already exactly as we need them, and the presence of the quantifiers does not interfere with the use of Biconditional Substitution. We do have to change the a in S_2 to b.

10. $\forall x[x \in b' \Leftrightarrow x \notin b]$ ‖

The previous proof can be used as a model for completing this one.
The next example shows that sometimes a universal theorem can be useful.

Theorem 27a: $\forall ab[a \cup b = \mathcal{1} \Leftrightarrow b' \subseteq a]$

Proof

1. $x \in \mathcal{1} \Rightarrow [[x \in a \lor x \in b \Leftrightarrow x \in \mathcal{1}] \Leftrightarrow$
$\qquad\qquad\qquad\qquad\qquad [x \notin b \Rightarrow x \in a]] \qquad \|$

Working as before, with Theorems 2a, 2b, and 2e, we arrive at

9. $[x \in a \cup b \Leftrightarrow x \in \mathcal{1}] \Leftrightarrow [x \in b' \Rightarrow x \in a] \quad \|$

We need $\forall x$ before the left-hand pair of brackets to be able to apply Theorem 3, and we also need it before the right-hand pair in order to apply the definition of $a \subseteq b$. Using Generalization gives us the quantifier overall, and then UT 16 allows us to distribute it over the biconditional. The rest is easy.

EXERCISES

1. Fill in the missing steps and justifications for the proof of Theorem 8b.

2. Complete the proof of Theorem 5 in detail.

3. Complete the proof of Theorem 27a in detail.

4. Use the proof of Theorem 8b as a model to construct a proof of Theorem 8a.

5. Prove Theorem 21a without using any theorem after Theorem 4.

6. Prove Theorem 17b without using any theorem after Theorem 4.

7. Prove Theorem 21b without using any theorem after Theorem 4.

Exercises based on nonstandard models: In Exercises 8 through 14, we will be referring to a nonstandard model of $\{\mathcal{1}, \in\}$. (Review Chapter 1, particularly § 1-5.) Let the objects represented by first-category terms be restricted to the numbers 3, 5, and 7, and let the second-category terms be restricted to the numbers 2, 6, 10, 14, 30, 42, 70, and 210. We interpret $x \in a$ by "x is a divisor of a." Thus $3 \in 6$ is a true statement, $5 \in 42$ is false, and "$6 \in 30$" is not a statement, because it violates the category restrictions.

8. There are 24 possible statements of the form $x \in a$, where the variables have been replaced by constants. List them, and state which are true in this model.

9. What are $\mathbf{t}$ and $\varnothing$ in this model? (You are limited to the numbers $2, 6, \ldots, 210$ listed above.)

10. **(a)** List all the values of x satisfying the condition $x \in 42$.
    (b) List the values satisfying $x \notin 42$.
    (c) Determine $42'$ from the relation $\forall x [x \in 42' \Leftrightarrow x \notin 42]$.
    (d) Make a table showing the value of a' for each a.

11. **(a)** List all values of x satisfying the condition $x \in 30 \cap 42$.
    (b) What is the value of a if $a = 30 \cap 42$?
    (c) Construct an 8 by 8 "multiplication" table for $a \cap b$.

12. **(a)** List all values of x satisfying the condition $x \in 30 \cup 42$.
    (b) What is the value of a if $a = 30 \cup 42$?
    (c) Construct an 8 by 8 "multiplication" table for $a \cup b$.

13. **(a)** List all values of b satisfying the condition $b \subseteq 70$.
    (b) For each value of b found in (a), verify that Theorems 12a and 12b hold by checking the values of $b \cap 70$ and $b \cup 70$ in the tables of Exercises 11 and 12.

14. Verify that Theorems 26a and 26b hold, using 30 and 70.

In Exercises 15 through 20, we shall use another nonstandard model. The first-category objects are the numbers 1 and -1, and the second-category objects are the four equations

$$e_1:\ n^2 + 1 = 0 \qquad e_3:\ n^3 + n^2 + n + 1 = 0$$
$$e_2:\ n^4 - 1 = 0 \qquad e_4:\ n^3 - n^2 + n - 1 = 0$$

$x \in a$ is to be interpreted by "x is a solution of a."

15. List all possible true statements of the form $x \in a$, where the variables have been replaced by constants. (The second-category constants are e_1, e_2, e_3, and e_4.)

16. What are $\mathbf{t}$ and $\varnothing$ in this model?

17. Make a table showing all a, a' pairs.

18. Construct a "multiplication" table for $a \cap b$.

19. Construct a "multiplication" table for $a \cup b$.

20. List all the true statements of the form $a \subseteq b$, where the variables have been replaced by constants. (You should find nine of them.)

Theorems 5 through 27b are of a rather restricted type with respect to quantification. The method used for their proof does not extend to all second-category theorems. Test your skill on the following theorems, using any theorem on the list as a "previous theorem."

21. Prove: $\forall a[\forall b[b \subseteq a] \Rightarrow a = 1]$

22. Prove: $\forall a[\exists b[b \cap a \neq \varnothing] \Rightarrow a \neq \varnothing]$

23. Prove: $\forall a[\exists b[b \subseteq a \wedge b' \subseteq a] \Leftrightarrow a = 1]$

Chapter 12

THE BOOLEAN APPROACH:

THE SYSTEM $\{ɫ, \cup, \cap\}$

12-1 INTRODUCTION

In this chapter we shall arrive at the same results that we did in Chapter 11, insofar as those results dealt solely with second-category terms. Now our only variables will be lowercase Latin letters from the front of the alphabet, and $\in$ will not be used at all. The approach will be noticeably different in at least two respects; it will be strongly algebraic in appearance, and the order in which the theorems are listed has been chosen to facilitate proofs in this system. The axioms and definitions of the system of Chapter 11 will not appear here at all, since they all involve the use of $\in$. However, every axiom and definition of $\{ɫ, \cup, \cap\}$ is provable in $\{ɫ, \in\}$.

Any system satisfying the axioms of this chapter is called a "Boolean algebra," after the English mathematician George Boole (1815–1864). He is generally considered to be the earliest creator of modern symbolic logic, and Boolean algebra is one of the outgrowths of his work in that field.

In addition to the variables described above, the symbols $\cup$ and $\cap$ will be used to form terms, for which we shall have the closure axioms 1a and 1b. Criteria for statements are exactly the same as those of § 11-3, except that (1) is omitted, together with the references to categories in that section.

Criteria for Statements

(1) ——————— = ——————— is a statement when both blanks are replaced by terms.

(2) ∃—[———————] is a statement if the left blank is replaced by a variable and the right blank is replaced by a statement.

(3)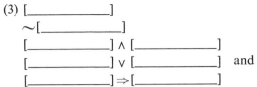

are each statements if the blanks are replaced by statements.

(4) Additional statement forms may be defined by giving permission to substitute a novel combination of symbols for a combination that already meets the criteria for a statement. The new form must exhibit as free variables all those and only those which occur free in the old form.

(5) For any combination of symbols to qualify as a statement, it must be constructible by a finite number of applications of the constructions (1) through (4).

As before, we shall take $\Leftrightarrow$, $\forall$, and $\exists_1$, as already defined, and we shall allow the usual scope conventions. (For details, see § 11-3.)

12-2   AXIOMS AND DEFINITIONS

We start with four closure axioms, asserting the unique existence of certain objects.

Axiom 1a: $\forall ab \exists_1 c[c = a \cup b]$
     1b: $\forall ab \exists_1 c[c = a \cap b]$
     2a: $\exists_1 a \forall b[b \cap a = b]$
     2b: $\exists_1 a \forall b[b \cup a = b]$

Axioms 2a and 2b clearly describe constants. (Why?) These constants will be needed for Axiom 3, so we define them at this point.

Definitions

     $\maltese$: $\forall a[a = \maltese \Leftrightarrow \forall b[b \cap a = b]]$
     $\varnothing$: $\forall a[a = \varnothing \Leftrightarrow \forall b[b \cup a = b]]$

The next axiom is also a closure axiom, leading again to a definition.

Axiom 3: $\forall b \exists_1 a[a \cup b = \maltese \wedge a \cap b = \varnothing]$

Definition

$$b': \quad \forall ba[a = b' \Leftrightarrow a \cup b = \text{Ӏ} \wedge a \cap b = \varnothing]$$

The next group of four axioms should have a familiar aspect, even if you skipped Chapter 11.

> **Axiom 4a:** $\forall ab[a \cup b = b \cup a]$ ⎫
>   **4b:** $\forall ab[a \cap b = b \cap a]$ ⎬ (Commutative Laws)
>   **5a:** $\forall abc[a \cup (b \cap c) = (a \cup b) \cap (a \cup c)]$ ⎫ (Left
>   ⎬ Distributive
>   **5b:** $\forall abc[a \cap (b \cup c) = (a \cap b) \cup (a \cap c)]$ ⎭ Laws)

In the real number system, both addition and multiplication are similarly commutative. Multiplication is distributive over addition, but addition is not generally distributive over multiplication. In the present system, each operation is distributive over the other. Another pair of statements resembling laws of numbers will be found in Theorems 17a and 17b.

We wish to define the statement form $a \subseteq b$, but the definition of Chapter 11 is unusable here. (Why?) Instead, we take our cue from Theorem 12 of that chapter.

Definition

$$\text{``}a \subseteq b\text{''} \quad \text{for} \quad \text{``}a \cup b = b\text{''}$$

The final axiom is

Axiom 6: $\text{Ӏ} \neq \varnothing$

It will not be used in this chapter, and all the theorems presented here can be proved without it. As shown in the exercise that follows § 12-3, it is needed to ensure that there is more than one object in the system. By Exercise 2 of § 11-6, it also ensures that the system $\{ \text{Ӏ}, \cup, \cap \}$ is consistent with the system $\{ \text{Ӏ}, \in \}$.

EXERCISES

For Exercises 1 through 7, we shall use the following nonstandard model:

Let the objects represented by the terms of $\{ \text{Ӏ}, \cup, \cap \}$ be restricted to the numbers 1, 3, 5, 7, 15, 21, 35, and 105.

~Let $a \cap b$ mean "the greatest common divisor of a and b."

Let $a \cup b$ mean "the least common multiple of a and b."

1. Write a "multiplication" table showing the values of $a \cup b$ for all possible combinations of values of a and b.

2. Same as Exercise 1, for $a \cap b$.

3. Write a list of all true statements of the form $a \subseteq b$, where the variables have been replaced by constants. Use the table of Exercise 1 and the definition of $a \subseteq b$.

4. What are $\mathbf{1}$ and $\varnothing$ in this model?

5. (a) Show that $5' = 21$.
   (b) List all a, a' pairs.
   (c) What is the algebraic relationship between a and a'?

6. Verify that Axioms 5a and 5b hold with the following sets of values:
   (a) $a = 1, b = 5, c = 35$.
   (b) $a = 105, b = 35, c = 21$.
   (c) $a = 5, b = 5, c = 21$.

7. Can you see a close connection between this model and the standard one? The given list of constants is not a random choice!

In Exercises 8 through 11, our model will have just two objects in it: the numbers 0 and 1. Let $a \cap b$ represent the numerical product ab, and let $a \cup b$ represent the computation indicated by the algebraic formula $a + b - ab$.

8. Check each of the axioms for this model. In checking Axiom 1a, for example, you will have to show that the c mentioned is uniquely determined as 0 or as 1 for all four possible assignments of values to a and b.

9. (a) What are $\mathbf{1}$ and $\varnothing$ in this model?
   (b) Make a list of the a, a' pairs.
   (c) Find an algebraic interpretation of the relation of a to a'.

10. Write all possible statements of the form $a \subseteq b$, where the variables have been replaced by constants.

11. (a) Complete the following table to show values of a', $a \cup b$, $a \cap b$, and $a' \cup b$ for all four possible assignments of values to a and b.

a	b	a'	$a \cup b$	$a \cap b$	$a' \cup b$
1	1				
1	0				
0	1				
0	0				

(b) What amazing fact do you discover in the patterns of this table?

(c) Can you add another interesting column?

12-3 A LIST OF THEOREMS

Theorem 1a: $\exists_1 a[a = \maltese]$
1b: $\exists_1 a[a = \varnothing]$
1c: $\forall b \exists_1 a[a = b']$

Theorems 1a, 1b, and 1c are the ones that validate the use of $\maltese$, $\varnothing$, and b' as terms. (The use of $a \cup b$ and $a \cap b$ was validated by Axioms 1a and 1b.)

Theorem 2a: $\forall abc[a = b \Rightarrow a \cup c = b \cup c]$
2b: $\forall abc[a = b \Rightarrow a \cap c = b \cap c]$
2c: $\forall abcd[a = b \wedge c = d \Rightarrow a \cup c = b \cup d]$
2d: $\forall abcd[a = b \wedge c = d \Rightarrow a \cap c = b \cap d]$

The four parts of Theorem 2 are simple applications of UT 19 (see § 10-10), analogous to simple rules of ordinary algebra. *The converses of Theorems 2a through 2d do not hold!*

Theorem 3a: $\forall a[a \cap \maltese = a]$
3b: $\forall a[a \cup \varnothing = a]$
3c: $\forall a[a \cup a' = \maltese]$
3d: $\forall a[a \cap a' = \varnothing]$

The four parts of Theorem 3 state the defining properties of $\dagger$, $\varnothing$, and a' in a form convenient to use in later proofs. If we start with the relevant definition, each part takes only four or five steps to prove.

The remaining list by no means exhausts all possibilities. By experimentation the reader may discover some interesting theorems for himself.

Theorem 4a: $\forall ab[(a \cup b) \cap (a \cup b') = a]$

4b: $\forall ab[(a \cap b) \cup (a \cap b') = a]$

5a: $\forall a[a \cup a = a]$

5b: $\forall a[a \cap a = a]$

6: $\forall ab[a \cup b = b \Leftrightarrow b \cap a = a]$

7a: $\forall ab[a \subseteq b \Leftrightarrow a \cup b = b]$

7b: $\forall ab[b \subseteq a \Leftrightarrow a \cap b = b]$

8: $\forall ab[a = b \Leftrightarrow a \subseteq b \wedge b \subseteq a]$

9: $\forall a[a \subseteq a]$

10: $\forall abc[a \subseteq b \wedge b \subseteq c \Rightarrow a \subseteq c]$

11a: $\forall a[a \subseteq \dagger]$

11b: $\forall a[\varnothing \subseteq a]$

12a: $\forall a[a \cup \dagger = \dagger]$

12b: $\forall a[a \cap \varnothing = \varnothing]$

13a: $\forall ab[a \subseteq a \cup b]$

13b: $\forall ab[a \cap b \subseteq a]$

14a: $\forall abc[a \subseteq b \Rightarrow a \cup c \subseteq b \cup c]$

14b: $\forall abc[b \subseteq a \Rightarrow b \cap c \subseteq a \cap c]$

15a: $\forall abcd[a \subseteq b \wedge c \subseteq d \Rightarrow a \cup c \subseteq b \cup d]$

15b: $\forall abcd[b \subseteq a \wedge d \subseteq c \Rightarrow b \cap d \subseteq a \cap c]$

16a: $\forall abc[a \subseteq c \wedge b \subseteq c \Rightarrow a \cup b \subseteq c]$

16b: $\forall abc[c \subseteq a \wedge c \subseteq b \Rightarrow c \subseteq a \cap b]$

17a: $\forall abc[a \cup (b \cup c) = (a \cup b) \cup c]$ (Associative

17b: $\forall abc[a \cap (b \cap c) = (a \cap b) \cap c]$ Laws)

18: $\forall a[a = (a')']$

19: $\forall ab[a' = b' \Leftrightarrow a = b]$

20: $\forall ab[a = b' \Leftrightarrow a' = b]$

21a: $\forall ab[(a \cup b)' = a' \cap b']$

21b: $\forall ab[(a \cap b)' = a' \cup b']$ (De Morgan's Laws)

22: $\forall ab[a \subseteq b \Leftrightarrow b' \subseteq a']$

23a: $\forall ab[a = b' \Leftrightarrow a \cup b = a' \cup b']$

23b: $\forall ab[a = b' \Leftrightarrow a \cap b = a' \cap b']$

24a: $\forall ab[a \cup b = \dagger \Leftrightarrow b' \subseteq a]$

24b: $\forall ab[a \cap b = \varnothing \Leftrightarrow a \subseteq b']$

EXERCISE

Let Σ be the system $\{\check{1}, \cup, \cap\}$, but with Axiom 6 omitted. Prove as a theorem of Σ, $\check{1} = \varnothing \Leftrightarrow \forall a[a = \check{1}]$. Since Axiom 6 is not needed for the proofs of any of the theorems on the list, you may use any of them as assumptions.

12-4 MOVES TOWARD INFORMALITY

It is a nuisance, and not particularly illuminating at this stage, to go through the steps necessary in applying the commutative laws to get every possible trivial commutation of the other axioms, definitions, and theorems. So, without further ado, we shall assume the presence of corollaries to every pertinent axiom, definition, or theorem, inverting the order of pairs of terms joined by $\cup$ or $\cap$. thus

$$\forall a[a = \check{1} \Leftrightarrow \forall b[a \cap b = b]]$$

can be called a definition of $\check{1}$. We may use "Th 3d" as an acceptable reference for

$$\forall a[a' \cup a = \check{1}]$$

You may assume no fewer than 32 different forms of Axiom 5a without even using the symmetry of equality.

We shall go further. In view of UT 17, we need not worry about distinguishing between $\alpha = \beta$ and $\beta = \alpha$. At times we shall also identify $P \wedge Q$ with $Q \wedge P$, $P \vee Q$ with $Q \vee P$, and $P \Leftrightarrow Q$ with $Q \Leftrightarrow P$ (but never $P \Rightarrow Q$ with $Q \Rightarrow P$!!!). After all, if anyone does blow the whistle on us, we can quickly make everything strictly legal.

In contrast with the proofs of the same theorems in Chapter 11, we are going to use the list of the preceding section in the usual sequential way. For example, in proving Theorem 6 we shall have Theorems 3b, 3d, and 4a as steps. Keeping this in mind, let us look at some typical proofs.

Theorem 6: $\forall ab[a \cup b = b \Leftrightarrow b \cap a = a]$

We shall use a standard method for proving this biconditional, the method that uses two lemmas and the Biconditional Theorem.

Lemma A: $a \cup b = b \vdash b \cap a = a$

Proof: The "previous theorem" that looks as though it might help with this lemma is Theorem 4a.

1. $\forall ab[(a \cup b) \cap (a \cup b') = a]$	Th 4a
2. $(a \cup b) \cap (a \cup b') = a$	Inst $a \to a, b \to b$

Our assumption now can simplify this.

3. $a \cup b = b$	As
4. $b \cap (a \cup b') = a$	Eq Sub S_3, S_2

The Distributive Law will give us the term $b \cap a$.

5. $\forall abc[a \cap (b \cup c) = (a \cap b) \cup (a \cap c)]$	Ax 5b
6. $b \cap (a \cup b') = (b \cap a) \cup (b \cap b')$	Inst $a \to b, b \to a, c \to b'$

Theorem 3d will wash out the $b \cap b'$, with the help of 3b.

7. $\forall a[a \cap a' = \varnothing]$	Th 3d
8. $b \cap b' = \varnothing$	Inst $a \to b$
9. $b \cap (a \cup b') = (b \cap a) \cup \varnothing$	Eq Sub S_8, S_6
10. $\forall a[a \cup \varnothing = a]$	Th 3b
11. $(b \cap a) \cup \varnothing = b \cap a$	Inst $a \to b \cap a$
12. $b \cap (a \cup b') = b \cap a$	Eq Sub S_{11}, S_9
13. $b \cap a = a$	Eq Sub S_{12}, S_4

A proof for the converse lemma could easily be constructed by mimicking the proof of Lemma A, interchanging b for a in all free occurrences, $\varnothing$ with $\mathcal{X}$, and $\cap$ with $\cup$. The first two steps would then be:

1. $\forall ab[(a \cap b) \cup (a \cap b') = a]$	Th 4b
2. $(b \cup a) \cup (b \cap a') = b$	Inst $a \to b, b \to$

Instead of following this plan, we are going to use Lemma B to illustrate the technique of the continued equality, another big step away from formality. In it, we omit the formal statement of axioms, definitions, or previous theorems, merely referring to them in the justification column. This naturally eliminates explicit use of Instance. Nor is Equality Substitution explicitly mentioned, although, like Instance, it is implicit in the whole process.

Lemma B: $b \cap a = a \vdash a \cup b = b$

Proof

1. $a \cup b = (a \cup b) \cap t$	Th 3a
2. $\quad = (a \cup b) \cap (a \cup a')$	Th 3c
3. $\quad = a \cup (b \cap a')$	Ax 5a
4. $\quad = (b \cap a) \cup (b \cap a')$	As
5. $\quad = b$	Th 4b

One can read this as a run-on sentence, "$a \cup b$ equals $(a \cup b) \cap t$, which equals $(a \cup b) \cap (a \cup a')$, which equals $\cdots$ which equals b." Alternatively, one could consider "$a \cup b$" as understood on the left side of each equation, including the last. The theorem itself now follows from these two lemmas by the Biconditional Theorem and Generalization.

It might be instructive to compare the two proofs with regard to what is included and what is omitted in the justification column.

Theorems 5a and 5b also lend themselves to this technique.

Theorem 5a: $\forall a[a \cup a = a]$

Proof

1. $a \cup a = (a \cup a) \cap t$	Th 3a
2. $\quad = (a \cup a) \cap (a \cup a')$	Th 3c
3. $\quad = a$	Th 4a
4. $\forall a[a \cup a = a]$	Gen ⓐ

Theorem 5b: $\forall a[a \cap a = a]$

Proof

1. $a \cap a = (a \cap a) \cup \varnothing$	Th 3b
2. $\quad = (a \cap a) \cup (a \cap a')$	Th 3d
3. $\quad = a$	Th 4b
4. $\forall a[a \cap a = a]$	Gen $\textcircled{a}$

The continued equality can be used only in certain circumstances. We shall, however, continue at that level of informality for the last illustration, omitting full statement of axioms and so on. Any use of Choice or Generalization cannot be so lightly treated, because of their restrictions and after-effects, and therefore must be explicitly noted.

Theorem 17a: $\forall abc[a \cup (b \cup c) = (a \cup b) \cup c]$

Proof: Theorem 8 provides one of the most used ways of proving two sets equal, that is, by proving that each is a subset of the other. Hence our first goal will be to prove that $a \cup (b \cup c) \subseteq (a \cup b) \cup c$. The devices used in 1 through 6 are typical of proofs in Boolean algebra.

1. $a \subseteq a \cup b$	Th 13a
2. $a \cup b \subseteq (a \cup b) \cup c$	Th 13a
3. $a \subseteq (a \cup b) \cup c$	Th 10
4. $b \subseteq a \cup b$	Th 13a
5. $b \cup c \subseteq (a \cup b) \cup c$	Th 14a
6. $a \cup (b \cup c) \subseteq (a \cup b) \cup c$	Th 16a S_3, S_5

Now for the reverse inclusion, using the same devices.

7. $c \subseteq b \cup c$	Th 13a
8. $b \cup c \subseteq a \cup (b \cup c)$	Th 13a
9. $c \subseteq a \cup (b \cup c)$	Th 10
10. $b \subseteq b \cup c$	Th 13a
11. $a \cup b \subseteq a \cup (b \cup c)$	Th 14a
12. $(a \cup b) \cup c \subseteq a \cup (b \cup c)$	Th 16a S_9, S_{11}

Now we apply Theorem 8.

13. $a \cup (b \cup c) = (a \cup b) \cup c$ $\qquad \Big\| $ Th 8 S_6, S_{12}

Three steps of Generalization complete the proof.

16. $\forall abc[a \cup (b \cup c) = (a \cup b) \cup c]$ $\qquad \Big\| $ Gen ⓐ

EXERCISE

Explain how the 32 different forms of Axiom 5a can arise from using the commutativity of $\cap$ and of $\cup$.

12-5 THE DUALITY PRINCIPLE FOR $\{t, \cap, \cup\}$

Let us return to the proofs of Theorems 5a and 5b. Just as the theorems resemble each other closely, so do their proofs. In this system, we can even dispense with one of the two proofs.

If you examine the axioms of our system, you will find that by taking any "a" axiom, interchanging $\cap$ with $\cup$, and t with $\varnothing$, you arrive at the corresponding "b" axiom. Performing this operation on Axiom 3 leaves it essentially unchanged. Axiom 1b is said to be the "dual" of Axiom 1a, and vice versa. If we split Axiom 3 in two by this prescription, we get

Axiom 3a: $\forall b \exists_1 a[a \cup b = t \wedge a \cap b = \varnothing]$
3b: $\forall b \exists_1 a[a \cap b = \varnothing \wedge a \cup b = t]$

According to the informal identification of "$P \wedge Q$" with "$Q \wedge P$" allowed in § 12-4, we see that Axioms 3a and 3b are effectively identical. Statements like Axiom 3 are said to be "self-dual." If we note that Theorems 7a and 7b prescribe "$\beta \subseteq \alpha$" as the dual of "$\alpha \subseteq \beta$," even a statement like Theorem 10 can be considered self-dual. Writing it in dual versions, we get

Theorem 10a: $\forall abc[a \subseteq b \wedge b \subseteq c \Rightarrow a \subseteq c]$
10b: $\forall abc[b \subseteq a \wedge c \subseteq b \Rightarrow c \subseteq a]$

After commuting the substatements of the antecedent in 10b, we have

$\forall abc[c \subseteq b \wedge b \subseteq a \Rightarrow c \subseteq a]$

This last is equivalent to Theorem 10a by UT 5 and UT 8. In other words, Theorem 10b can be shown to be logically equivalent to Theorem 10a by methods that have nothing to do with the structure of $\{ \bar{}, \cup, \cap \}$.

Since for each axiom or definition there is a dual axiom or definition, it is clear that the proof of any theorem can be dualized to produce a proof of the dual theorem. The list of theorems has been arranged to show their duality. Every "a" and "b" pair is a dual pair. So are the pairs 2c–2d and 3c–3d. Theorem 1c is trivially self-dual. The proofs of Theorems 5a and 5b, as given in the preceding section, provide an illustration of a dual pair of proofs. All this is by way of an informal proof of the following metatheorem:

> *The Duality Principle:* For every statement S of the system $\{ \bar{}, \cup,$ $\cap \}$, let S^* be the statement formed by interchanging $\bar{}$ with $\varnothing$, and $\cup$ with $\cap$, and substituting the statement $\beta \subseteq \alpha$ for every substatement of the form $\alpha \subseteq \beta$, including, possibly, S itself. Then $A_1, A_2, \ldots, A_m \vdash P$ if and only if $A_1{}^*, A_2{}^*, \ldots, A_m{}^* \vdash P^*$. In particular, P is a theorem of $\{ \bar{}, \cup, \cap \}$ if and only if P^* is.

Other mathematical systems have similar duality structures, notably projective geometry and algebraic topology. The statement calculus exhibits a duality that is closely linked to that of this chapter, if we restrict the sentential operators to negation, conjunction, and disjunction. (To see how this can be done, refer to § 3-7.) It is not too surprising that this should be so, in view of the close connection between subset theorems and tautologies that we found in Chapter 11. We have left further exploration of this as an exercise (see Exercise 8).

EXERCISES

Write the dual of each of the statements in Exercises 1 through 6.

1. $\forall ac [a \cap b \subseteq b \cup c]$

2. $a \cap (b \cup c) = b \Rightarrow b' \subseteq a$

3. $a \subseteq b \Leftrightarrow b \subseteq c \vee b' = \varnothing$

4. $\forall ab [a \subseteq b \Rightarrow a' \cup b = \bar{} \wedge a' \cap b = \varnothing]$

5. $\forall a [a \neq \bar{} \Rightarrow \exists b [b \neq \varnothing \wedge b \subseteq a']]$

6. $\forall a[\exists b[a \cup b = \prime] \wedge \exists c[a \cap c = \varnothing]]$

7. Which of the above statements could be considered to be self-dual?

8. The following duality theorem can be proved for the sentential calculus†:

> Let S and T be sentential formulas that use only negation, conjunction, and disjunction. Let $\bar{S}$ and $\bar{T}$ be formed from S and T, respectively, by writing $\vee$ for $\wedge$, and vice versa. Then $S \Rightarrow T$ is tautological if and only if $\bar{T} \Rightarrow \bar{S}$ is tautological, and $S \Leftrightarrow T$ is tautological if and only if $\bar{S} \Leftrightarrow \bar{T}$ is.

In the list of tautological formulas given in § 3-6, there are several pairs that fit the above description. Find them.

In Exercises 9 through 12, you may use any of the listed theorems as a "previous theorem."

9. Prove: $\forall a[\forall b[a \subseteq b] \Rightarrow a = \varnothing]$.

10. Prove: $\forall a[\exists b[b \cup a \neq \prime] \Rightarrow a \neq \prime]$.

11. Prove: $\forall a[\exists b[a \subseteq b \wedge a \subseteq b'] \Leftrightarrow a = \varnothing]$.

12. Prove: $\forall a[a \neq \prime \Rightarrow \exists b[b \neq \varnothing \wedge a \cap b = \varnothing]]$.

13. See how far you can get in proving the whole list of subset theorems. If you really get stuck at any one of them, assume that you have proved it, and go on to the next.

---

† For a discussion of this, see J. B. Rosser, *Logic for Mathematics* (New York: McGraw-Hill, 1953), pp. 117ff.

ANSWERS TO ODD-NUMBERED

EXERCISES†

1-2 Definitions and Undefined Expressions

1. For example, if we call the activity of repairing automobiles "mathematics," and people who work at automobile repair "mathematicians," then we have satisfied the requirement that the characteristic activity of mathematicians is mathematics, and that mathematics is what mathematicians do.

3. (a) Logically unimpeachable.
(b) Psychologically, we usually prefer that a derived word such as "mathematician" be defined in terms of the more basic word "mathematics." Logically, this is not necessary, and in mathematics we sometimes disregard that principle, as in the definition of a "finite set" as "a set which is not infinite" (R. Dedekind, 1883).
(c) From a practical standpoint, one could object that, on the one hand, many practicing mathematicians (e.g., in the Soviet Union) might not be members of those organizations, and, on the other hand, one only has to pay dues to belong to them.

5. This writer does not know of any. If you think that you have found one, please look it up in the Oxford Unabridged Dictionary before you send it to me.

1-6 Mathematical Systems

1.+ In base six numeration, $2 \times 5 = 14$.

3. In an operational sense. The postulates delimit what can be done with the undefined terms.

2-2 Sentential Variables and Sentential Formulas

1. Statement. 3. Statement. 5. Imperative sentence, not a statement. 7. Statement (the exclamation point is a mathematical symbol here). 9. Statement. 11. Interrogative sentence, not a statement.

2-3 Negation

1. For "b is an irrational number" to be a general negation of "b is a rational number," the first statement would have to be true whenever the second is

† Answers marked with + have more than one correct variant.

181

false. If *b* is used to represent the Washington Monument, then both statements are false.

3. It would depend on what basic table is agreed upon for the operator $\sim$. With the following table, $\sim\sim P$ and P would not be interchangeable, since $\sim\sim P$ would have the value F when P has the value T.

P	$\sim P$
T	M
M	F
F	T

2-4 Conjunction and Disjunction

1. + "moreover," "nevertheless," "in addition to which."

2-5 The Conditional

1. It rains $\Rightarrow$ it pours.

3. One should buy yachts $\Rightarrow$ one is rich.

5. (a) It is equilateral $\Rightarrow$ a triangle is isosceles; (b) a triangle is equilateral $\Rightarrow$ it is isosceles.

7. x is real $\Rightarrow$ when y . . . is $x + y$.

9. I behold . . . sky $\Rightarrow$ my heart leaps up.

11. Not a conditional.

13. For the formula $P \Rightarrow Q$, we have:

When P, Q.	(1), (8)
If P, then Q.	(2), (7)
P only if Q.	(3), (5b)
For P, it is necessary that Q.	(4a)
For Q, it is sufficient that P.	(4b)
Q if P.	(5a)
Q when P.	(9)

2-6 The Biconditional

"P is a necessary and sufficient condition for Q." (From a standpoint of strict grammatical usage, this should be "That P . . . condition that Q.")

2-7 Brackets and Scope Conventions. Sentential Operators

1. $\sim P \vee [Q \Rightarrow P]$

3. $\sim [P \wedge Q] \Rightarrow P \vee Q \vee R$

5. $[P \Rightarrow P \wedge Q] \Rightarrow Q$

7. $[P \Leftrightarrow Q] \Leftrightarrow R \Rightarrow S$

9. $[P \wedge [\sim Q]] \Rightarrow [P \wedge [R \wedge S]]$

11. $Q \Rightarrow [[P \vee R] \Rightarrow [[\sim P] \Rightarrow [\sim R]]]$

13. $[P \Rightarrow [R \vee S]] \Leftrightarrow [[\sim P] \vee [R \vee S]]$

15. $[[\sim P] \Rightarrow Q] \Leftrightarrow [[\sim Q] \Rightarrow P]$

17. P: ABC is a triangle

Q: $\overline{AD}$ bisects angle A

R: $\dfrac{BD}{CD} = \dfrac{AB}{AC}$

S: $(AD)^2 = (AC)(AB) - (AD)(CD)$

Formula: $P \wedge Q \Rightarrow R \wedge S$

19. P: $|\sin^2 x_1 - \sin^2 x_2| < k$

Q: $|x_1 - x_2| < h$

R: $k > 0$

S: $h < \dfrac{k}{2}$

Formula: $R \wedge S \Rightarrow Q \Rightarrow P$

21. P: $\lim f = a$

Q: $\lim g = b$

R: $\lim fg = ab$

S: $b \neq 0$

T: $\lim \dfrac{f}{g} = \dfrac{a}{b}$

Formula: $P \wedge Q \Rightarrow R \wedge [S \Rightarrow T]$

23. P: $x < 0$

Q: $x^2 > 0$

R: $x > 0$

S: $x = 0$

Formula: $[P \Rightarrow Q] \wedge [R \Rightarrow Q] \Rightarrow [\sim S \Rightarrow P \vee R] \Rightarrow S \vee Q$

25. P: $x + y$ is rational

Q: x is rational

R: y is rational

Formula: $P \Rightarrow [Q \wedge R] \vee [\sim Q \wedge \sim R]$

27. (a) 2; (b) 5.

Remark: The general formula for n letters is

$$\frac{1}{4n - 2} \binom{2n}{n} \quad \text{or} \quad \frac{1}{4n - 2} \frac{(2n)!}{(n!)^2}$$

3-1 Basic Truth Tables

1. (a), (b) inclusive; (c), (d), (e) exclusive.

3. (Both parts have the same table.)

P	Q	$P \underline{\vee} Q$
T	T	F
T	F	T
F	T	T
F	F	F

3-2   Truth Tables for Compound Sentences

Final columns should read, top to bottom, as follows:

1. T T T T

3. T F T T

5. T T F T

7. T T T T

3-3   Tautologies

1. Formula: $P \wedge Q \Rightarrow R \wedge S$. The statement is false when P and Q are both true and one or both of R and S is false.

3. To be provable in plane geometry means that they may be proved using the axioms and definitions as assumptions. These axioms and definitions cannot affect the tautological or nontautological nature of a statement.

5. $Q \Rightarrow P$

7. $\sim[Q \wedge R]$

3-4   A Short Test for Tautology

1. Table 1c; Table 1a; consistency with previous steps; Table 1d

3. Tautology

5. Tautology

7. Tautology

9. The formula has the value F for two combinations:

P	Q	R
T	T	T
T	F	T

3-5   Choice of Formulas

1. Formula: $[P \wedge Q \Rightarrow R] \Rightarrow [\sim Q \Rightarrow \sim R]$. It is false for two combinations:

P	Q	R
T	F	T
F	F	T

3. Formula: $[R \wedge \sim S \Rightarrow [P \wedge Q] \vee [\sim P \wedge \sim Q]] \wedge \sim [\sim P \wedge \sim Q \Rightarrow \sim R]$. It is true for just two combinations:

P	Q	R	S
F	F	T	T
F	F	T	F

5. Formula: $P \vee Q \Rightarrow [\sim P \Rightarrow Q]$. It is tautological.

7. No. Let $\mathcal{F}$ be a formula that correctly represents the statement, even if some of the sentential variables used in $\mathcal{F}$ do not represent independent substatements. If $\mathcal{F}$ is tautological, we may have tested some combinations which could not occur with the given statement, but those which could occur would still give the value T in each case.

3-6   Useful Tautological Formulas

1. $\mathcal{S} \Leftrightarrow \mathcal{C}$ is a short way of writing $[\mathcal{S} \Rightarrow \mathcal{C}] \wedge [\mathcal{C} \Rightarrow \mathcal{S}]$. For this to be true, neither bracketed statements can take the value F (see Table 1b). Hence each one must be tautological.

3. + One should look for statements P, Q, and R, such that R is false, and P or Q, *but not both*, is false.

3-7   Reducing the Number of Basic Operators

1. $P \Leftrightarrow Q$ for $\sim [P \wedge \sim Q] \wedge \sim [Q \wedge \sim P]$

3. $P \wedge Q$ for $\sim [P \Rightarrow \sim Q]$; $P \vee Q$ for $\sim P \Rightarrow Q$; $P \Leftrightarrow Q$ for $\sim [[P \Rightarrow Q] \Rightarrow \sim [Q \Rightarrow P]]$

5. $\sim P$ for $P \mid P$; $P \wedge Q$ for $P \mid Q \parallel P \mid Q$; $P \vee Q$ for $P \mid P \parallel Q \mid Q$; $P \Rightarrow Q$ for $P \parallel Q \mid Q$; (+) $P \Leftrightarrow Q$ for $P \parallel Q \parallel\mid P \mid P \parallel Q \mid Q$

7. You should get results completely analogous to those of Exercises 4, 5, and 6. For instance, $P * Q$ is equivalent to $\sim[P \vee Q]$, just as $P \mid Q$ is equivalent to $\sim[P \wedge Q]$.

4-1   Quantifiers

1. $\sim \forall x \exists y [P \Rightarrow \forall z \sim Q]$

3. $\forall x \sim \forall y [P \vee Q]$

5. $[[\forall x [\forall y P]] \vee [\exists x Q]] \Rightarrow [[\forall y R] \wedge S]$

7. $\sim [\exists y [\forall x [\forall t [Q \vee R]]]] \wedge [[\forall z P] \Rightarrow S]$

9. + P should express a relation between x and y such that for each x, the relation is satisfied for a *limited* collection of y's.

11. (a) $\sim \forall x P$ is equivalent to $\exists x \sim P$, $\forall x \sim P$ is equivalent to $\sim \exists x P$, $\sim \forall x \sim P$ is equivalent to $\exists x P$; (b) whenever $\forall x P$ and $\forall x \sim P$ are both false, then $\sim \forall x P$ and $\sim \forall x \sim P$ are both true. But these last are equivalent respectively to $\exists x \sim P$ and $\exists x P$.

4-3   Purifying Quantifiers

1. + P: s is positive Q: q is a real number
       R: r is a real number S: s is a real number
       T: $q = r$ U: $q^2 = s$
       W: $r^2 = s$

Formula: $\forall s [P \wedge S \Rightarrow \exists qr [Q \wedge R \wedge \sim T \wedge U \wedge W]]$

3. P: e is a vector Q: f is a vector
    R: $e = f$ S: $ae + bf = 0$
    T: $a = 0$ U: $b = 0$

Formula: $\exists ef [P \wedge Q \wedge \sim R \wedge \forall ab [S \Rightarrow T \wedge U]]$

5. P: x_0 is in the interval (a, b)

$$Q: \lim_{h \to 0} \frac{f(x_0 + h) - f(x_0)}{h} = y$$

Formula: $\forall x_0 [P \Rightarrow \exists y Q]$

7. + P: $f(x_0) = y$ Q: $f(x_0) = z$ R: $y = z$

Formula: $\exists y [P \wedge \forall z [Q \Rightarrow R]]$

9. For every x and y, if $x < y$, there is a z such that $x < z$ and $z < y$.

11. + For every m and n, if m is a line and n is a line, then there exists a p such that p is a point and p is on m and p is on n.

13. + For all a, b, c, if abc is a right triangle and $\not\prec abc$ is a right angle, then $(ab)^2 + (bc)^2 = (ac)^2$.

15. + For every x, if x is a prime integer, then there exists a y such that y is a prime integer and $y > x$.

4-4 Atomic Statements

1. $x > 0$, $y < x$, $y^2 > 0$

3. $x \in a$, $a = \{x \mid x \in a\}$

5. $x > 0$, $y \in \{x \mid x > 0\}$, $x < 0$, $z \in \{x \mid x < 0\}$, $z^2 < y$

4-5 Terms

1. 2, $2 + y$, y, 3, $3 + y$

3. x, a, b, $\{x \mid x \in a \lor x \in b\}$, y, $\{y \mid y \in a \lor y \in b\}$

5. A, π, r, 2, r^2, πr^2

7. m, n, $m \cap n$, $\emptyset$

4-7 Bound Variables and Free Variables

	Constants	Bound Variables	Free Variables
1.	2, 3	none	y
3.	none	x, y	a, b
5.	π	none	A, r
7.	$\emptyset$	m, n	none

4-8 Predicate Notation

1. Dictionary: $P(x)$: x is a point. $Q(x, y)$: $x = y$. $R(x, y, z)$: x, y, and z are collinear. $S(x)$: x is a plane. $T(x, y)$: $x \in y$.

Formula: $\forall xyz[P(x) \land P(y) \land P(z) \land {\sim}Q(x, y) \land {\sim}Q(y, z) \land {\sim}Q(z, x) \land {\sim}R(x, y, z) \Rightarrow {\sim}\exists mn[S(m) \land S(n) \land {\sim}Q(m, n) \land T(x, m) \land T(y, m) \land T(z, m) \land T(x, n) \land T(y, n) \land T(z, n)]]$

3. $\forall xy[G(x, y) \Rightarrow \exists z[G(x, z) \land G(z, y)]]$

5. $\forall xy[R(x) \land R(y) \Rightarrow [Q(xy, 0) \Leftrightarrow Q(x, 0) \lor Q(y, 0)]]$

7. + $\forall xy[R(x) \land R(y) \Rightarrow [{\sim}Q(x, y) \Leftrightarrow G(x, y) \lor G(y, x)]]$

9. $\forall xyef[R(x) \land R(y) \land W(e) \land W(f) \Rightarrow W(xe + yf)]$

11. + $\forall xy[R(x) \wedge R(y) \wedge \sim Q(x, y) \Rightarrow \exists z[T(z) \wedge [[G(x, z) \wedge G(z, y)] \vee [G(y, z) \wedge G(z, x)]]]]$

13. + $\sim \exists x[P(x) \wedge \forall y[P(y) \Rightarrow \sim G(y, x)]]$, or, equivalently, $\forall x[P(x) \Rightarrow \exists y[P(y) \wedge G(y, x)]]$

15. $\forall f[C(f, a, b) \Rightarrow \exists x[B(x, a, b) \wedge \forall y[B(y, a, b) \Rightarrow \sim G(f(y), f(x))]]]$

17. $P(1) \wedge \forall k[P(k) \Rightarrow P(k + 1)] \Rightarrow \forall n P(n)$

19. (a) For an example, $P(x, y)$: x is married to y; (b) for an example, $P(x, y)$: x is the father of y.

4-9   Special Pairs of Statement Forms

1. $P(z) — P(y)$

3. $P(y) — P(\alpha)$, $\alpha = y + 2$

5. + $P(\alpha) — P(\beta)$, $P(z)$: $z + x^2 = y^2$, $\alpha = x$, $\beta = y$.

7. $P(\alpha) — P(y)$, $\alpha = x$

9. This pair fits none of the descriptions.

11. + $P(\alpha) — P(\beta)$, $P(z)$: $\forall x[x^2 > 0] \Rightarrow z > 0$, $\alpha = (x - y)^2$, $\beta = (t - x)^2$

13. + $P(z)$: $2 + 2 = z$, $\alpha = \beta = 4$

5-4   Rules of Instance and Example

1. Any statement illustrating the necessity for the restrictions on one rule will, by using its negation, provide an illustration for the necessity of the restrictions on the other rule.

3. Formula: $\forall x[M(x) \Rightarrow \exists y[\sim M(y) \wedge B(y, x)]]$
If we apply Instance, with $x \to y$, and then Detachment, we get the formula: $M(y) \Rightarrow \exists y[\sim M(y) \wedge B(y, y)]$. This says, "If y is a man, then there is a woman who gave birth to herself." [The y in the first "$M(y)$" does not necessarily have any relation to the bound y's.]

5-7   The Rule of Detachment

If P is a true statement, and also $P \Rightarrow S_i$, then S_i cannot be false, since that would make $P \Rightarrow S_i$ false. So if we have already been permitted to assert P and $P \Rightarrow S_i$, we may safely assert S_i.

5-9   Three Sample Demonstrations

1.   (a) Yes

(b) $\sim P(y) \Rightarrow \forall x \sim P(x)$	Gen $\textcircled{y}$
$[\sim P(y) \Rightarrow \forall x \sim P(x)] \Rightarrow \sim \forall x \sim P(x) \Rightarrow P(y)$	Tau
$\sim \forall x \sim P(x) \Rightarrow P(y)$	Det

(c) $\sim \forall x \sim P(x)$ is equivalent to $\exists x P(x)$. (See Exercise 11 of § 4-1.) Hence the last statement in (b) is equivalent to $\exists x P(x) \Rightarrow P(y)$. Thus we have obtained a statement of the form given in the Rule of Choice without actually using that rule.

(d) The Rule of Instance may be similarly derived from the Rule of Example, or vice versa.

3.   30. $S_{20} \Rightarrow S_{28} \Rightarrow [P(x) \Rightarrow \exists m[L(m) \wedge C(x, m)]]$
    31. $S_{28} \Rightarrow [P(x) \Rightarrow \exists m[L(m) \wedge C(x, m)]]$

5.+

1. $\exists x \forall y[x + y = y]$	As
2. $S_1 \Rightarrow \forall y[x + y = y]$	Ch $\textcircled{x}$
3. $\forall y[x + y = y]$	Det S_1, S_2
4. $S_3 \Rightarrow x + y = y$	Inst $y \rightarrow y$
5. $x + y = y$	Det S_3, S_4
6. $S_5 \Rightarrow \exists x[x + y = y]$	Exam $x \rightarrow x$
7. $\exists x[x + y = y]$	Det S_5, S_6
8. $S_7 \Rightarrow \forall y \exists x[x + y = y]$	Gen $\textcircled{y}$
9. $\forall y \exists x[x + y = y]$	Det S_7, S_8

7.+

1. $\exists x \forall y[x = y + 1]$	As
2. $S_1 \Rightarrow \forall y[x = y + 1]$	Ch $\textcircled{x}$
3. $\forall y[x = y + 1]$	Det S_1, S_2
4. $S_3 \Rightarrow x = 1 + 1$	Inst $y \rightarrow 1$
5. $x = 1 + 1$	Det S_3, S_4
6. $S_3 \Rightarrow x = 2 + 1$	Inst $y \rightarrow 2$
7. $x = 2 + 1$	Det S_3, S_6
8. $x = 1 + 1 \Rightarrow [x = 2 + 1$ $\Leftrightarrow 1 + 1 = 2 + 1]$	Eq Sub
9. $S_5 \Rightarrow S_7 \Rightarrow S_8 \Rightarrow [1 + 1 = 2 + 1]$	Tau
10. $S_7 \Rightarrow S_8 \Rightarrow [1 + 1 = 2 + 1]$	Det S_5, S_9
11. $S_8 \Rightarrow [1 + 1 = 2 + 1]$.	Det S_7, S_{10}
12. $1 + 1 = 2 + 1$	Det S_8, S_{11}

9.

1. $\exists x \forall y [P(y) \Leftrightarrow x = y]$	As
2. $S_1 \Rightarrow \forall y [P(y) \Leftrightarrow x = y]$	Ch $\circledx$
3. $\forall y [P(y) \Leftrightarrow x = y]$	Det S_1, S_2
4. $S_3 \Rightarrow [P(x) \Leftrightarrow x = x]$	Inst $y \rightarrow x$
5. $P(x) \Leftrightarrow x = x$	Det S_3, S_4
6. $x = x$	Ref Eq
7. $S_5 \Rightarrow S_6 \Rightarrow P(x)$	Tau
8. $S_6 \Rightarrow P(x)$	Det S_5, S_7
9. $P(x)$	Det S_6, S_8
10. $P(x) \Rightarrow \exists x P(x)$	Exam $x \rightarrow x$
11. $\exists x P(x)$	Det S_9, S_{10}

11. Most of the steps are exactly described by the justifications. The key steps are:

6. $S_5 \Rightarrow [P(y) \Rightarrow x = y]$
10. $S_3 \Rightarrow [P(x) \Leftrightarrow x = x]$
12. $x = x$
13. $S_{11} \Rightarrow S_{12} \Rightarrow S_9 \Rightarrow [P(x) \wedge \forall y [P(y) \Rightarrow x = y]]$

5-10 Equivalence Relations

1. The only step that might give trouble is:

4. $xRx \Rightarrow \exists y [xRy]$

3. **(a)** The tautology would have the form

$P \Rightarrow [P \Rightarrow Q] \Rightarrow [P \wedge Q \Rightarrow R] \Rightarrow R$

(b) You should have checked to see whether you might be violating the restrictions on Generalization in specifying x.

5. If the directions are followed, key steps would be:

1. $\forall xy [\forall z [z \in \langle x \rangle \Leftrightarrow z \in \langle y \rangle] \Rightarrow \langle x \rangle = \langle y \rangle]$	As
5. $\forall z [z \in \langle x \rangle \Leftrightarrow x \in \langle y \rangle] \Rightarrow \langle x \rangle = \langle y \rangle$	Det S_3, S_4
6. $\langle x \rangle = \langle y \rangle \Rightarrow [z \in \langle x \rangle \Leftrightarrow z \in \langle y \rangle]$	Eq Sub
7. $[z \in \langle x \rangle \Leftrightarrow z \in \langle y \rangle] \Rightarrow \forall z [z \in \langle x \rangle \Leftrightarrow z \in \langle y \rangle]$	Gen $\circledz$, x, y
8. $S_5 \Rightarrow S_6 \Rightarrow S_7 \Rightarrow [\forall z [z \in \langle x \rangle \Leftrightarrow z \in \langle y \rangle] \Leftrightarrow \langle x \rangle = \langle y \rangle]$	Tau

Now three steps of detachment, followed by generalization on y and then on x (two steps for each), completes the job.

7. If we try to use x and y where we have used s and t, then the third use of Instance, with $x \rightarrow y$, would violate a restriction, since the y would become bound.

9.+ Key steps:

1. $\forall xy[x \in \langle y \rangle \Rightarrow \langle x \rangle = \langle y \rangle]$	As P_{10}
5. $x \in \langle y \rangle \Rightarrow \langle x \rangle = \langle y \rangle$	Det S_3, S_4
6. $\langle x \rangle = \langle y \rangle \Rightarrow [x \in \langle x \rangle \Leftrightarrow x \in \langle y \rangle]$	Eq Sub
7. $\forall x[x \in \langle x \rangle]$	As P_7
9. $x \in \langle x \rangle$	Det S_7, S_8
10. $S_5 \Rightarrow S_6 \Rightarrow S_9 \Rightarrow [x \in \langle y \rangle \Leftrightarrow \langle x \rangle = \langle y \rangle]$	Tau

6-2 The Lemma Theorem

i_1. (Given)	Inst $x \rightarrow x'$
i_2. (Given)	Eq Sub
i_3. $S_{i_1} \Rightarrow S_{i_2} \Rightarrow [\forall x_1 x_2 \cdots x_n[\alpha = \beta]$ $\Rightarrow [P'(\alpha') \Leftrightarrow P'(\beta')]]$	Tau
i_4. $S_{i_2} \Rightarrow [\forall x_1 x_2 \cdots x_n[\alpha = \beta]$ $\Rightarrow [P'(\alpha') \Leftrightarrow P'(\beta')]]$	Det S_{i_1}, S_{i_3}
i_5. $\forall x_1 x_2 \cdots x_n[\alpha = \beta] \Rightarrow [P'(\alpha')$ $\Leftrightarrow P'(\beta')]$	Det S_{i_2}, S_{i_4}

6-4 Three Corollaries

1. In the demonstration that $A_1, A_2, \ldots, H \vdash C$, strike out any occurrence of H as a step other than the first one. This will not invalidate the demonstration, since any use of Detachment which depended on H as a previous step can still be made, by changing the reference in the justification column, if necessary. The revised demonstration will fit the description of $\mathfrak{D}_2$ in the proof of the Deduction Theorem, so the existence of $\mathfrak{D}_3$ is assured.

3. (a) In the construction of $\mathfrak{D}_3$, steps justified as the assumption H (S_1 in Example 1) were replaced by the tautology $H \Rightarrow H$, resulting in no increase in the number of steps. However, if the justification was Choice, Detachment, or Example, the step is replaced by a three-step sequence. There are eight such steps in the demonstration of Example 1, thus giving 25 steps in all.

The first seven steps are:

1. $\exists xy[xy = yx] \Rightarrow \exists xy[xy = yx]$	Tau
2. $\exists xy[xy = yx] \Rightarrow \exists y[xy = yx]$	Ch $\widehat{x}$
3. $S_2 \Rightarrow [\exists xy[xy = yx] \Rightarrow S_2]$	Tau
4. $\exists xy[xy = yx] \Rightarrow S_2$	Det S_2, S_3
5. $S_1 \Rightarrow S_4 \Rightarrow [\exists xy[xy = yx] \Rightarrow S_2]$	Tau
6. $S_4 \Rightarrow [\exists xy[xy = yx] \Rightarrow S_2]$	Det S_1, S_5
7. $\exists xy[xy = yx] \Rightarrow S_2$	Det S_4, S_6

(b) Looking at S_4 and S_7, we can see a lot of waste motion. The nine-step proof starts by using S_2, S_4, S_6, and S_8, of the original demonstration as the first four steps, which we shall call $S_{1'}$, $S_{2'}$, $S_{3'}$, and $S_{4'}$. Then $S_{5'}$ is:

$S_{1'} \Rightarrow S_{2'} \Rightarrow S_{3'} \Rightarrow S_{4'} \Rightarrow [\exists xy[xy = yx]$ $\Rightarrow \exists yx[xy = yx]]$	Tau

Four uses of Detachment bring us to the desired statement at step $9'$.

5. By the Deduction Theorem, if $A_1, A_2, \ldots, A_n, P \vdash Q$, and also $B_1, B_2, \ldots, B_m, Q \vdash P$, then $A_1, A_2, \ldots, A_n \vdash P \Rightarrow Q$, and also $B_1, B_2, \ldots, B_m \vdash Q \Rightarrow P$. The conditions on the Biconditional Theorem then guarantee that the conditions on the Conjunction Theorem are also met, so we can assert that $A_1, A_2, \ldots, B_1, B_2, \ldots, B_m \vdash [P \Rightarrow Q] \wedge [Q \Rightarrow P]$, which is the Biconditional Theorem.

7. **(a)** T is a theorem of Σ only if $B_1, B_2, \ldots, B_n \vdash T$, where $B_1, \ldots, B_n$ represent the postulates and definitions of Σ. Then by n uses of the meta-theorem of Exercise 2 above, we get $\vdash B \Rightarrow T$; **(b)** in this sense, there is none. Each system is a collection of exercises in formal logic.

7-3   Inference Rule Forms of Several Rules

1. Subject to the same restrictions as given for the Rule of Choice in Chapter 5, the rule $\dfrac{\exists xP(x)}{P(y)}$ is admissible.

Proof: Let S_i be a step obtained by use of this rule. Then S_i is $P(y)$, and there was a previous step $\exists xP(x)$ such that $P(x)$ and $P(y)$ satisfied the conditions for a use of the Rule of Choice. We can therefore substitute the following two-step sequence for S_i:

$i_1.$ $\exists xP(x) \Rightarrow P(y)$	Ch $\widehat{y}$
$i_2.$ $P(y)$	Det

3. With descriptions and restrictions corresponding to those given in Chapter 5 for the Rules of Example, Equality Substitution, and Biconditional Substitution, respectively, the rules

$$\frac{P(\alpha)}{\exists x P(x)}, \qquad \frac{\forall x_1 x_2 \cdots x_m[\alpha = \beta]}{P(\alpha) \Leftrightarrow P(\beta)}, \qquad \text{and}$$

$$\frac{\forall x_1 x_2 \cdots x_m[R \Leftrightarrow S]}{P \Leftrightarrow Q} \quad \text{are each admissible.}$$

5. Let S_i be a step obtained by the use of the new rule. Then S_i is Q, and there were previous steps S_j: $\forall x_1 x_2 \cdots x_n[R \Leftrightarrow S]$ and S_k: P, with R, S, P, and Q satisfying the description and restrictions given in Chapter 5 for a use of the Rule of Biconditional Substitution. We can therefore substitute the following five-step sequence for S_i.

i_1.	$\forall x_1 x_2 \cdots x_n[R \Leftrightarrow S] \Rightarrow [P \Leftrightarrow Q]$	Bi Sub
i_2.	$P \Leftrightarrow Q$	Det S_j, S_{i_1}
i_3.	$[P \Leftrightarrow Q] \Rightarrow [P \Rightarrow Q]$	Tau
i_4.	$P \Rightarrow Q$	Det S_{i_2}, S_{i_3}
i_5.	Q	Det S_k, S_{i_4}

Thus we can obtain Q without using the new rule.

7. Let S_i be a step obtained by the use of the new rule. Then S_i is $\exists x P(x)$, and there was a previous step S_j: $\exists x[P(x) \wedge Q(x)]$. We can substitute the following sequence of six steps, where x' is a new variable, not needed elsewhere in the proof.

i_1.	$S_j \Rightarrow P(x') \wedge Q(x')$	Ch $\widehat{x'}$
i_2.	$P(x') \wedge Q(x')$	Det S_j, S_{i_1}
i_3.	$S_{i_2} \Rightarrow P(x')$	Tau
i_4.	$P(x')$	Det S_{i_2}, S_{i_3}
i_5.	$P(x') \Rightarrow \exists x P(x)$	Exam $x' \to x$
i_6.	$\exists x P(x)$	Det S_{i_4}, S_{i_5}

Thus we can obtain $\exists x P(x)$ without use of the new rule.

9. (We abbreviate the formal statement of the proof as given in the preceding examples.)

Previous statements: S_j: $\exists x P(x)$
$\qquad\qquad\qquad\quad$ S_k: $\forall x[P(x) \Rightarrow Q(x)]$
Derived statement: S_i: $\exists x Q(x)$

Substitute sequence:

$i_1.$ $\exists x P(x) \Rightarrow P(x')$	Ch (x')
$i_2.$ $P(x')$	Det S_j, S_{i_1}
$i_3.$ $\forall x[P(x) \Rightarrow Q(x)] \Rightarrow [P(x') \Rightarrow Q(x')]$	Inst $x \to x'$
$i_4.$ $P(x') \Rightarrow Q(x')$	Det S_k, S_{i_3}
$i_5.$ $Q(x')$	Det S_{i_2}, S_{i_4}
$i_6.$ $Q(x') \Rightarrow \exists x Q(x)$	Exam $x' \to x$
$i_7.$ $\exists x Q(x)$	Det S_{i_5}, S_{i_6}

7-4 Iterated Use of Instance and Example

In steps 4, 5, and 6 we might be in conflict with other uses of Choice or Generalization. A particular variable will be "needed" in a demonstration that $A_1, A_2, \ldots, A_n \vdash P$ only if it occurs free in one of the A_i's or in P, since these statements cannot be changed.

7-5 The Tautological Inference Family

1.

1. $\exists xy[xy = yx]$	As
2. $\exists y[xy = yx]$	Ch (x)
3. $xy = yx$	Ch (y) x
4. $\exists yx[xy = yx]$	Exam $x \to x,\ y \to y$

3. This is the Rule of Detachment itself, and so was not listed among those rules which are proved by use of the Rule of Detachment.

5. + We first prove

$$P_{11}, \exists z[z \in \langle x \rangle \wedge z \in \langle y \rangle] \vdash \langle x \rangle = \langle y \rangle$$

1. $\forall xy[x \in \langle y \rangle \Leftrightarrow \langle x \rangle = \langle y \rangle]$	As, P_{11}
2. $z \in \langle x \rangle \Leftrightarrow \langle z \rangle = \langle x \rangle$	Inst $x \to z,\ y \to x$
3. $z \in \langle y \rangle \Leftrightarrow \langle z \rangle = \langle y \rangle$	Inst S_1, $x \to z,\ y \to y$
4. $\exists z[z \in \langle x \rangle \wedge z \in \langle y \rangle]$	As
5. $z \in \langle x \rangle \wedge z \in \langle y \rangle$	Ch (z) x, y
6. $\langle z \rangle = \langle x \rangle \Rightarrow [\langle z \rangle = \langle y \rangle \Leftrightarrow \langle x \rangle = \langle y \rangle]$	Eq Sub
7. $\langle x \rangle = \langle y \rangle$	Tau Inf S_2, S_3, S_5, S_6

Hence, by the Deduction Theorem, there is a demonstration that $P_{11} \vdash \exists z[z \in \langle x \rangle \wedge z \in \langle y \rangle] \Rightarrow \langle x \rangle = \langle y \rangle$. Since no variable previously specified is free in P_{11} or in the last statement of the latter demonstration, we may generalize with x and y, thus obtaining a demonstration that $P_{11} \vdash \forall xy[\exists z[z \in \langle x \rangle \wedge z \in \langle y \rangle \Rightarrow \langle x \rangle = \langle y \rangle]]$.

7. Not admissible. $[P \Rightarrow Q] \Rightarrow Q \Rightarrow P$ is false when P is false and Q is true.

9. Admissible, $Q \vee R \Rightarrow P \vee {\sim}R \Rightarrow {\sim}Q \Rightarrow P$ is tautological.

11. You have an infinite choice!

13. The more obvious extensions are given below.

$$(1) \quad \frac{P_1}{P_1 \vee \cdots \vee P_n} \qquad (4) \quad \frac{P_1 \wedge \cdots \wedge P_n}{P_1}$$

$$(9) \quad \frac{P_1 \Rightarrow \cdots \Rightarrow P_n \Rightarrow R}{P_1 \wedge \cdots \wedge P_n \Rightarrow R}$$

$$(11) \quad \frac{P_1, P_2, \ldots, P_n}{P_1 \wedge P_2 \wedge \cdots \wedge P_n}$$

$$(16) \quad \frac{P_1 \Rightarrow P_2, P_2 \Rightarrow P_3, \ldots, P_n \Rightarrow R}{P_1 \Rightarrow R}$$

$$(17) \quad \frac{P \Rightarrow Q_1, P \Rightarrow Q_2, \ldots, P \Rightarrow Q_n}{P \Rightarrow Q_1 \wedge Q_2 \wedge \cdots \wedge Q_n}$$

$$(18) \quad \frac{P_1 \Rightarrow Q, P_2 \Rightarrow Q, \ldots, P_n \Rightarrow Q}{P_1 \vee P_2 \vee \cdots \vee P_n \Rightarrow Q}$$

$$(19) \quad \frac{P, P \Rightarrow Q_1, Q_1 \Rightarrow Q_2, \ldots, Q_n \Rightarrow R}{R}$$

$$(20) \quad \frac{P \Rightarrow Q_1, Q_1 \Rightarrow Q_2, \ldots, Q_n \Rightarrow R, {\sim}R}{{\sim}P}$$

$$(21) \quad \frac{P_1 \Rightarrow P_2, P_2 \Rightarrow P_3, \ldots, P_n \Rightarrow P_1}{P_i \Leftrightarrow P_j} \quad (\text{any } i, j)$$

7-6 Generalized Versions of Certain Rules

If P is an assumption, we cannot substitute y_i for z_i, as directed in the proof of this rule, since it would then not be one of the given (and immutable) assumptions. The Rule of Detachment is the only one that directly involves more than a single statement, and so the proof given for this rule would not work for it.

8-2 Some Particularly Useful Universal Theorems

1. (a) We would get a statement asserting "If every integer is even or odd" (which is true) "then every integer is even or every integer is odd" (which is false).

(b) We get, "If there is an odd integer and an even integer, then there is an even and odd integer." This statement is also false.

3. + Choose P and Q as unrelated statements about x, such that $\forall xP$ is true and $\forall xQ$ is false. For example, P might be $x = x$, and Q could be "x is happy."

5. + Choose P and Q as in Exercise 3, except that each should be true for some, but not all, values of x. For example, P: x is a man, and Q: x is a woman.

8-4 Formal Proof

1. Reasons, Part One: 1. As; 2. Inst $x \to x$; 3. Tau Inf; 4. Inst $x \to x'$; 5. Tau Inf; 6. Gen $\circledx$; 7. Gen x'; 8. Tau Inf S_6, S_7. Part Two: 1. As; 2. Tau Inf; 3. Tau Inf S_1; 4. Inst $S_2\, x \to x$; 5. Inst $S_3\, x \to x$; 6. Tau Inf S_4, S_5; 7. Gen $\circledx$.

3. (a) We cannot generalize twice (S_6 and S_7) on the same variable; (b) prove $\forall x[P \land Q] \vdash \forall xP$ by using steps 1, 2, 3, and 6 of the given proof. Then adapt this proof to show that $\forall x[P \land Q] \vdash \forall xQ$. Then the Conjunction Theorem gives the desired result.

5. + We first prove that $\forall xyP \vdash \forall yxP$.

1. $\forall xyP$	As
2. P	Inst $x \to x,\ y \to y$
3. $\forall xP$	Gen $\circledx y$
4. $\forall yxP$	Gen $\circledy$

Similarly, we show that $\forall yxP \vdash \forall xyP$. By the Biconditional Theorem, we have $\vdash \forall xyP \Leftrightarrow \forall yxP$. Since no variable specified in either proof is free in the last statement, we may generalize freely to get $\vdash \forall Z[\forall xyP \Leftrightarrow \forall yxP]$.

7. + We first prove that $\exists x\forall yP \vdash \forall y\exists xP$.

1. $\exists x\forall yP$	As
2. $\forall yP$	Ch $\circledx$
3. P	Inst $y \to y$
4. $\exists xP$	Exam $x \to x$
5. $\forall y\exists xP$	Gen $\circledy$

By the Deduction Theorem, $\vdash \exists x\forall yP \Rightarrow \forall y\exists xP$. Since no specified variables occur free in the last statement we may generalize freely to obtain $\vdash \forall Z[\exists x\forall yP \Rightarrow \forall y\exists xP]$.

9. + We observe that in UT 8, $P(x)$ is meant to represent any statement desired. In particular, it can be replaced by the negation of some statement. So we start with:

1. $\forall x \sim P(x) \Leftrightarrow \forall y \sim P(y)$	UT 8
2. $\forall x \sim P(x) \Leftrightarrow \sim \exists x P(x)$	UT 3
3. $\forall y \sim P(y) \Leftrightarrow \sim \exists y P(y)$	UT 3
4. $\exists x P(x) \Leftrightarrow \exists y P(y)$	Tau Inf S_1, S_2, S_3

No variables having been specified, we may generalize freely.

11.+ We shall use UT 12, and the same device used in the proof of UT 9, substituting $\sim P$ for P, and $\sim Q$ for Q.

1. $\forall x \sim P \vee \forall x \sim Q \Rightarrow \forall x [\sim P \vee \sim Q]$	UT 12
2. $\forall x [\sim P \vee \sim Q \Leftrightarrow \sim [P \wedge Q]]$	Tau
3. $\forall x \sim P \vee \forall x \sim Q \Rightarrow \forall x \sim [P \wedge Q]$	Bi Sub S_2, S_1
4. $\forall x \sim P \Leftrightarrow \sim \exists x P$	UT 3
5. $\forall x \sim Q \Leftrightarrow \sim \exists x Q$	UT 3
6. $\forall x \sim [P \wedge Q] \Leftrightarrow \sim \exists x [P \wedge Q]$	UT 3
7. $\exists x [P \wedge Q] \Rightarrow \exists x P \wedge \exists x Q$	Tau Inf S_3, S_4, S_5, S_6

No variables having been specified, we may generalize freely.

13.+ This one has a rather neat proof.

1. $P \Rightarrow \exists x P$	Exam $x \to x$
2. $[P \Rightarrow Q] \Rightarrow \exists x [P \Rightarrow Q]$	Exam $x \to x$
3. $\exists x Q \Rightarrow Q$	Ch $\circledx$
4. $[\exists x P \Rightarrow \exists x Q] \Rightarrow \exists x [P \Rightarrow Q]$	Tau Inf S_1, S_2, S_3

Since x is not free in S_4, we may generalize freely.

15.+ Proof of UT 17A:

1. $\alpha = \beta \Rightarrow [\alpha = \alpha \Leftrightarrow \beta = \alpha]$	Eq Sub
2. $\alpha = \alpha$	Ref Eq
3. $\alpha = \beta \Rightarrow \beta = \alpha$	Tau Inf S_1, S_2

Proof of UT 17B: Since α and β stand for any terms whatsoever, the converse of UT 17A is just another instance of 17A itself. So we may proceed thus:

1. $\alpha = \beta \Rightarrow \beta = \alpha$	UT 17A
2. $\beta = \alpha \Rightarrow \alpha = \beta$	UT 17A
3. $\alpha = \beta \Leftrightarrow \beta = \alpha$	Tau Inf S_1, S_2

No variables having been specified, so we may generalize freely.

17.   (a) +

1. $\forall xyP \Leftrightarrow \sim\exists x\sim\forall yP$	UT 1†
2. $\sim\forall yP \Leftrightarrow \exists x\sim P$	UT 2
3. $\forall xyP \Leftrightarrow \sim\exists xy\sim P$	Bi Sub†

(b) +

1. $\sim\forall xy\sim P \Leftrightarrow \exists x\sim\forall y\sim P$	UT 2†
2. $\sim\forall y\sim P \Leftrightarrow \exists yP$	UT 4
3. $\sim\forall xy\sim P \Leftrightarrow \exists xyP$	Bi Sub†

19.   (a) We start with a proof that $Q \Rightarrow \forall xP \vdash \forall x[Q \Rightarrow P]$:

1. $Q \Rightarrow \forall xP$	As
2. $\forall xP \Rightarrow P$	Inst $x \to x$
3. $Q \Rightarrow P$	Tau Inf S_1, S_2
4. $\forall x[Q \Rightarrow P]$	Gen ⓧ

By the Deduction Theorem, there is a demonstration that $\vdash [Q \Rightarrow \forall xP] \Rightarrow \forall x[Q \Rightarrow P]$. Since there are no specified variables occurring free in this last statement, we may generalize freely.

(b) At step 4, if there had been free occurrences of x in Q, we could not have generalized on x without violating the first restriction on the Rule of Generalization.

8-5   Applications in Group Theory

1.   (a) Both axioms hold for multiplication, when we exclude zero.

(b) The z (and w) whose existence is asserted for each x and y pair is $y \div x$.

(c) Using Instance, $x \to 0$, $y \to 1$, on Axiom 2, would give us the false statement $\exists z[0 * z = 1] \wedge \exists w[w * 0 = 1]$.

(d) Both axioms hold for addition, when we allow zero and negative numbers.

(e) + For example, the rational numbers, or the even integers.

3.   1. As (Temp); 2. Tau Inf; 3. Tau Inf S_1; 4. Ax 1; 5. Inst $x \to w$, $y \to x$, $z \to y$; 6. Eq Sub S_3, S_5; 7. Eq Sub S_2, S_6; 8. Th 3; 9. Inst $x \to y$; 10. Tau Inf S_9; 11. Inst S_8, $x \to w$; 12. Tau Inf S_{11}; 13. Eq Sub S_{10}, S_7; 14. Eq Sub S_{12}, S_{13}; 15. Ded. Th.; 16. Gen ⓦx, y; 17. Gen ⓨx

5.

1. $\forall y[y = u \Leftrightarrow \forall xP(x, y)]$	Def "u"
2. $u = u \Leftrightarrow \forall xP(x, u)$	Inst $y \to u$
3. $u = u$	Ref Eq
4. $\forall xP(x, u)$	Tau Inf S_2, S_3

† Remember that $\forall xyP$ and $\exists xyP$ are abbreviations for $\forall x[\forall yP]$ and $\exists x[\exists yP]$, respectively.

7.

1. $\forall xyz[(x * y) * z = x * (y * z)]$	Ax 1
2. $(x * y) * y^{-1} = x * (y * y^{-1})$	Inst $x \to x,\ y \to y,\ z \to y^{-1}$
3. $\forall x[x * x^{-1} = u \wedge x^{-1} * x = u]$	Th 5
4. $y * y^{-1} = u \wedge y^{-1} * y = u$	Inst $x \to y$
5. $y * y^{-1} = u$	Tau Inf S_4
6. $(x * y) * y^{-1} = x * u$	Eq Sub $S_5,\ S_2$

⌐ 7. $x * y = u$ As (Temp)

8. $u * y^{-1} = x * u$	Eq Sub $S_7,\ S_6$
9. $\forall x[x * u = x \wedge u * x = x]$	Th 3
10. $y^{-1} * u = y^{-1} \wedge u * y^{-1} = y^{-1}$	Inst $x \to y^{-1}$
11. $u * y^{-1} = y^{-1}$	Tau Inf S_{10}
12. $y^{-1} = x * u$	Eq Sub $S_{11},\ S_8$
13. $x * u = x \wedge u * x = x$	Inst $S_9,\ x \to x$
14. $x * u = x$	Tau Inf S_{13}
15. $y^{-1} = x$	Eq Sub $S_{13},\ S_{12}$
16. $y * y^{-1} = y * y^{-1}$	Ref Eq
17. $y * x = y * y^{-1}$	Eq Sub $S_{15},\ S_{16}$
18. $y * y^{-1} = u$	Tau Inf S_4
19. $y * x = u$	Eq Sub $S_{18},\ S_{17}$
20. $x * y = u \wedge y * x = u$	Tau Inf $S_7,\ S_{19}$
21. $\forall xy[y = x^{-1} \Leftrightarrow x * y = u \wedge y * x = u]$	Def "x^{-1}"

└22. $y = x^{-1}$ Bi Sub $S_{21},\ S_{20}$

23. $x * y = u \Rightarrow y = x^{-1}$	Ded Th
24. $\forall y S_{23}$	Gen Ⓨ x
25. $\forall xy S_{23}$	Gen Ⓧ

9.   **(a)**

1. $x * z = x * z$	Ref Eq
2. $x = y \Rightarrow [x * z = x * z \Leftrightarrow x * z$ $= x * y]$	Sub Eq
3. $x = y \Rightarrow x * z = y * z$	Tau Inf $S_1,\ S_2$

Conclude with three uses of Generalization.

(b)

1. $\forall xyz[x = y \Rightarrow x * z = y * z]$	Th 8a
2. $x * z = y * z \Rightarrow (x * z) * z^{-1} =$	
$\qquad\qquad\qquad\qquad (y * z) * z^{-1}$	Inst $x \to x * z$, $y \to y * z$, $z \to z^{-1}$
3. $\forall xyz[(x * y) * z = x * (y * z)]$	Ax 1
4. $(x * z) * z^{-1} = x * (z * z^{-1})$	Inst $x \to x$, $y \to z$, $z \to z^{-1}$
5. $(y * z) * z^{-1} = y * (z * z^{-1})$	Inst S_3, $x \to y$, $y \to z$, $z \to z^{-1}$
6. $\forall x[x * x^{-1} = u \wedge x^{-1} * x = u]$	Th 5
7. $z * z^{-1} = u \wedge z^{-1} * z = u$	Inst $x \to z$
8. $z * z^{-1} = u$	Tau Inf S_7
9. $(x * z) * z^{-1} = x * u$	Eq Sub S_8, S_4
10. $(y * z) * z^{-1} = y * u$	Eq Sub S_8, S_5
11. $\forall x[x * u = x \wedge u * x = x]$	Th 3
12. $x * u = x \wedge u * x = x$	Inst $x \to x$
13. $x * u = x$	Tau Inf S_{12}
14. $(x * z) * z^{-1} = x$	Eq Sub S_{13}, S_9
15. $y * u = y \wedge u * y = y$	Inst S_{11}, $x \to y$
16. $y * u = y$	Tau Inf S_{15}
17. $(y * z) * z^{-1} = y$	Eq Sub S_{16}, S_{10}
18. $x * z = y * z \Rightarrow x = (y * z) * z^{-1}$	Eq Sub S_{14}, S_2
19. $x * z = y * z \Rightarrow x = y$	Eq Sub S_{17}, S_{18}

Conclude with three steps of Generalization.
(c) Remove the quantifiers from Theorems 8a and 8b, then use Tau Inf to get the biconditional, and conclude with three steps of Generalization.
(d) $\forall xyz[z * x = z * y \Rightarrow x = y]$

9-2 The Basic Relations and Their Applications

1. $[P \vee Q] \wedge [\sim P \vee \sim R]$

3. $[S \wedge \sim P] \wedge [\sim P \wedge \sim S]$

5. $\exists x \forall y[P \Rightarrow \sim Q]$ or $\exists x \forall y[Q \Rightarrow \sim P]$ or $\exists x \forall y[\sim P \vee \sim Q]$

7. $\forall xyP \wedge \forall x[\exists yP \wedge \sim Q]$

9.+ $\forall x[P \wedge [\forall yQ \wedge \forall zR \Rightarrow \forall z \sim S]]$

11.   (a) Any formula with an even number of tildes is equivalent to the given one; (b) 8; (c) 8; (d) 4, 4. (e) There are 2^{n-1} formulas equivalent to the given one, and an equal number equivalent to its negation. An argument for this can be based on finite induction for $n \geq 2$, by considering $P_1 \Leftrightarrow [P_2 \Leftrightarrow P_3 \Leftrightarrow \cdots \Leftrightarrow P_{n+1}]$. If we assume that there are 2^{n-1} formulas having each truth value, which can be obtained by negating sentential variables within the bracket, then each of the possibilities P_1 and $\sim P_1$ gives us 2^{n-1} formulas with the value T and an equal number with the value F. Since the rule holds for $n = 2$, it holds for all $n \geq 2$.

13. (a) Truth tables for all three have identical last columns.
(b) If n is not divisible by 6, then it is not divisible by 3 or it is not divisible by 2; if n is divisible by 3 but not by 6, then it is not divisible by 2; if n is divisible by 2 but not by 6, then it is not divisible by 3.
(c) If abc does not have a 45° interior angle, then it is not an isosceles right triangle; if abc is an isosceles triangle and does not have a 45° interior angle, then it is not a right triangle; if abc is a right triangle and does not have a 45° interior angle, then it is not isosceles.

15. (a) $\forall x[N \Rightarrow [\sim R \Leftrightarrow \sim D]]$. (b) The most natural one is $\forall x[N \Rightarrow [R \Leftrightarrow D]]$. (c) Any real number is rational if and only if it can be represented by a repeating decimal.

17. (a) Some negative number has a nonpositive square. (b) $\forall x[N(x) \wedge G(0, x) \Rightarrow G(x^2, 0)]$. (c) $\exists\, x[N(x) \wedge G(0, x) \wedge \sim G(x^2, 0)]$.

19. (a) There is an integer n, greater than 2, such that $x^n + y^n = z^n$ has a solution in integers. (b) $\forall n[J(n) \wedge G(n, 2) \Rightarrow \sim \exists xyz[J(x) \wedge J(y) \wedge J(z) \wedge x^n + y^n = z^n]]$. (c) $\exists n[J(n) \wedge G(n, 2) \wedge \exists xyz[J(x) \wedge J(y) \wedge J(z) \wedge x^n + y^n = z^n]]$.

21. (a)+ There is a positive number without a unique positive cube root. (b) $\forall x[N(x) \wedge G(x, 0) \Rightarrow \exists_1 y[G(y, 0) \wedge y^3 = x]]$. (c)+ $\exists x[N(x) \wedge G(x, 0) \wedge \forall y[G(y, 0) \wedge y^3 = x \Rightarrow \exists z[G(z, 0) \wedge z^3 = x \wedge y \neq z]]]$.

10-3 Terms by Postulate

1. Line, plane

10-5 Terms by Definition

1. Using the first form given in § 10-2, you would need the Rules of Choice and Tautological Inference. Using the second form, you would need Choice, Instance, Reflexivity of Equality, and Tautological Inference.

3.+   1. $\forall x \exists_1 z[z = F(x, y)]$ As (7)
          This permits using $F(x, y)$ as a term.

    2. $\forall x \forall z[z = F(x, y)$
                  $\Leftrightarrow z = (x + y) \sin x/\cos y$ As (13)

    3. $F(x, y) = F(x, y) \Leftrightarrow F(x, y)$
                  $= (x + y) \sin x/\cos y$ Inst $x \to x$, $z \to F(x, y)$

    4. $F(x, y) = F(x, y)$ Ref Eq

    5. $F(x, y) = (x + y) \sin x/\cos y$ Tau Inf S_3, S_4

    6. $\forall x[F(x, y) = (x + y) \sin x/\cos y]$ Gen $\widehat{x}\, y$

10-7 Defining New Statement Forms

(a) We can state $\forall ab[\forall x[x \in a \Leftrightarrow x \in b] \Leftrightarrow \forall x[x \in a \Leftrightarrow x \in b]]$ by the Rule of Tautology. Then the free substitution, applied to the left side of the main biconditional, gives us the second definition.

(b) If we use an inference rule form of Biconditional Substitution (see Exercise 5 of § 7-3) the second definition makes possible free substitution of one form for the other, since it is completely quantified.

10-9 More Formal Versions of Four Basic Rules

Rule of Example: S_i has the form

$$\exists_1 z[z = \alpha] \Rightarrow [P(\alpha) \Rightarrow \exists x P(x)]$$

(subject to the same restrictions as in Chapter 5). Rule of Equality Substitution: S_i has the form

$$\exists_1 z[z = \alpha] \wedge \exists_1 z[z = \beta] \Rightarrow [\forall x_1 x_2 \cdots x_n[\alpha = \beta] \Rightarrow [P(\alpha)$$

$$\Leftrightarrow P(\beta)]]$$

(subject to the same restrictions as in Chapter 5). Rule of Reflexivity of Equality: S_i has the form

$$\exists_1 z[z = \alpha] \Rightarrow \alpha = \alpha$$

10-10 A Theorem on Equality

1.   1. $\alpha = \beta \Rightarrow [\varphi(\alpha) = \varphi(\alpha) \Leftrightarrow \varphi(\alpha) = \varphi(\beta)]$ Eq Sub

    2. $\varphi(\alpha) = \varphi(\alpha)$ Ref Eq

    3. $\alpha = \beta \Rightarrow \varphi(\alpha) = \varphi(\beta)$ Tau Inf

3.+ For instance, replace addition by subtraction or by multiplication. In positive numbers, we may also use division.

11-3 Criteria for Statements

1.   Statement

3. $a \subseteq b$ has not yet been defined.

5. m and n do not qualify as variables.

7.   Statement

9. $P(x)$ is not a statement of this system.

11-4 Axioms and Definitions

Regulation violated. $x \notin x$ is not a statement.

11-5 Some Simple Basic Theorems

1.   Theorem: $\exists x[x \in \mathcal{t}]$

Proof:

1. $\forall x[x \in \mathcal{t}]$	Th 2b
2. $x \in \mathcal{t}$	Inst $x \to x$
3. $\exists x[x \in \mathcal{t}]$	Exam $x \to x$

3.
1. $\forall b \exists_1 a \forall x[x \in a \Leftrightarrow \sim[x \in b]]$	Ax 2
2. $\forall ab[a = b' \Leftrightarrow \forall x[x \in a \Leftrightarrow \sim[x \in b]]]$	Def b'
3. $\forall b \exists_1 a[a = b']$	Bi Sub

5.
1. $\forall bc \exists_1 a \forall x[x \in a \Leftrightarrow x \in b \vee x \in c]]$	Ax 5
2. $\forall abc[a = b \cup c \Leftrightarrow \forall x[x \in a$ $\Leftrightarrow x \in b \vee x \in c]]$	Def $b \cup c$
3. $\forall bc \exists_1 a[a = b \cup c]$	Bi Sub

7.
1. $\forall ab[a = b' \Leftrightarrow \forall x[x \in a \Leftrightarrow x \notin b]]$	Def b'
2. $a' = a' \Leftrightarrow \forall x[x \in a' \Leftrightarrow x \notin a]$	Inst $a \to a', b \to a$
3. $a' = a'$	Ref Eq
4. $\forall x[x \in a' \Leftrightarrow x \notin a]$	Tau Inf S_2, S_3
5. $\forall ax[x \in a' \Leftrightarrow x \notin a]$	Gen $\circled{x}$

9.+

1. $\forall ab[a = b' \Leftrightarrow \forall x[x \in a \Leftrightarrow x \notin b]]$	Def b'
2. $\emptyset = ł' \Leftrightarrow \forall x[x \in \emptyset \Leftrightarrow x \notin ł]$	Inst $a \to \emptyset$, $b \to ł$
3. $\emptyset = ł'$	Def $\emptyset$
4. $\forall x[x \in \emptyset \Leftrightarrow x \notin ł]$	Tau Inf S_2, S_3
5. $x \in \emptyset \Leftrightarrow x \notin ł$	Inst $x \to x$
6. $\forall x[x \in ł]$	Th 2b
7. $x \in ł$	Inst $x \to x$
8. $x \notin \emptyset$	Tau Inf S_5, S_7
9. $\forall x[x \notin \emptyset]$	Gen $\textcircled{x}$

11.

1. $\forall abc[a = b \cup c \Leftrightarrow \forall x[x \in a$ $\Leftrightarrow x \in b \vee x \in c]]$	Def $b \cup c$
2. $a \cup b = a \cup b \Leftrightarrow \forall x[x \in a \cup b$ $\Leftrightarrow x \in a \vee x \in b]$	Inst $a \to a \cup b$, $b \to a$, $c \to b$
3. $a \cup b = a \cup b$	Ref Eq
4. $\forall x[x \in a \cup b \Leftrightarrow x \in a \vee x \in b]$	Tau Inf S_2, S_3
5. $\forall bx[x \in a \cup b \Leftrightarrow x \in a \vee x \in b]$	Gen $\textcircled{b}$, a
6. $\forall abx[x \in a \cup b \Leftrightarrow x \in \vee x \in b]$	Gen $\textcircled{a}$

11-6 Membership and Equality

(a)

1.+

1. $\forall ab[a = b \Leftrightarrow \forall x[x \in a \Leftrightarrow x \in b]]$	Th 3
2. $a = b \Leftrightarrow \forall x[x \in a \Leftrightarrow x \in b]$	Inst $a \to a$, $b \to b$
3. $\sim\forall x[x \in a \Leftrightarrow x \in b] \Leftrightarrow \exists x \sim[x \in a$ $\Leftrightarrow x \in b]$	UT 2
4. $\forall x[\sim[x \in a \Leftrightarrow x \in b] \Leftrightarrow [x \in a \wedge x \notin b]$ $\vee [x \notin a \wedge x \in b]]$	Tau
5. $\sim\forall x[x \in a \Leftrightarrow x \in b] \Leftrightarrow \exists x[[x \in a$ $\wedge x \notin b] \vee [x \notin a \wedge x \in b]]$	Bi Sub S_4, S_3
6. $a \neq b \Leftrightarrow \exists x[[x \in a \wedge x \notin b]$ $\vee [x \notin a \wedge x \in b]]$	Tau Inf S_2, S_5

Complete with two steps of Generalization.

(b) If two sets are unequal, then one of them has an element which is not in the other.

3. Justifications for Lemma A: 1. As; 2. Tau; 3. Eq Sub; For Lemma B: 3. Inst; 4. Ch©, b; 5. Inst; 6. As; 7. Tau Inf S_5, S_6; 8. Inst S_4, $a \rightarrow b$; 9. Tau; 10. Tau Inf S_8, S_9; 11. Eq Sub S_7, S_{10}.

5.

1. $\forall ab [a = b \Leftrightarrow \forall x [[x \in a \Rightarrow x \in b]$ $\wedge [x \in b \Rightarrow x \in a]]]$	Th 3
2. $\forall ab [\forall x [[x \in a \Rightarrow x \in b] \wedge [x \in b$ $\Rightarrow x \in a]] \Leftrightarrow \forall x [x \in a \Rightarrow x \in b]$ $\wedge \forall x [x \in b \Rightarrow x \in a]]$	UT 10

(Note: $\forall Z$ is represented here by $\forall ab$.)

3. $\forall ab [a = b \Leftrightarrow \forall x [x \in a \Rightarrow x \in b]$ $\wedge \forall x [x \in b \Rightarrow x \in a]]$	Bi Sub S_2, S_1

By the definition of $\subseteq$, this is the desired statement.

11-7 Subset Theorems and Tautologies

To change an "a" theorem into a "b" theorem, and vice versa, (1) interchange $\cup$ and $\cap$, (2) replace $\alpha \subseteq \beta$ with $\beta \subseteq \alpha$, and (3) interchange $\mathbf{1}$ and $\varnothing$. Theorems having just one form shown do not change significantly in this process.

11-8 Illustrative Proofs

1. Justification for proof of Th 8b: 1. Tau; 2. Th 2d; 3. Th 2e; 4. Inst S_2 $a \rightarrow a$, $b \rightarrow b$, $x \rightarrow x$; 5. Inst S_2 $a \rightarrow a$, $b \rightarrow c$, $x \rightarrow x$; 6. Inst S_3 $a \rightarrow b$, $b \rightarrow c$, $x \rightarrow x$; 7. Inst S_2 $a \rightarrow a$, $b \rightarrow b \cup c$, $x \rightarrow x$; 8. Inst S_3 $a \rightarrow a \cap b$, $b \rightarrow a \cap c$, $x \rightarrow x$; 9. Bi Sub S_4, S_1; 10. Bi Sub S_5, S_9; 11. Bi Sub S_6, S_{10}; 12. Bi Sub S_7, S_{11}; 13. Bi Sub S_8, S_{12}; 14. Gen $\circledx a$, b, c; 15. Th 3; 16. Inst S_{15} $a \rightarrow a \cap (b \cup c)$, $b \rightarrow (a \cap b) \cup (a \cap c)$; 17. Tau Inf (or Bi Sub) S_{14}, S_{16}; 18. Gen ©a, b; 19. Gen ⓑa; 20 Gen ⓐ. (These justifications will easily determine the steps.)

3.+

1. (Given)	Tau
2. $\forall x [x \in \mathbf{1}]$	Th 2b
3. $\forall ax [x \in a' \Leftrightarrow x \notin a]$	Th 2a
4. $\forall abx [x \in a \cup b \Leftrightarrow x \in a \vee x \in b]$	Th 2e
5. $x \in \mathbf{1}$	Inst S_2 $x \rightarrow x$
6. $[x \in a \vee x \in b \Leftrightarrow x \in \mathbf{1}]$ $\Leftrightarrow [x \notin b \Rightarrow x \in a]$	Det S_5, S_1
7. $\forall x [x \in b' \Leftrightarrow x \notin b]$	Inst S_3 $a \rightarrow b$

8. $[x \in a \lor x \in b \Leftrightarrow x \in \dagger]$
$$\Leftrightarrow [x \in b' \Rightarrow x \in a] \quad\quad \text{Bi Sub } S_7, S_6$$

9. $[x \in a \cup b \Leftrightarrow x \in \dagger] \Leftrightarrow [x \in b' \Rightarrow x \in a]$ Bi Sub S_4, S_8

10. $\forall x S_9$ Gen $\circledx a, b$

11. $\forall x S_9 \Rightarrow [\forall x[x \in a \cup b \Leftrightarrow x \in \dagger]$
$$\Leftrightarrow \forall x[x \in b' \Rightarrow x \in a]] \quad\quad \text{UT } 16$$

12. $\forall x[x \in a \cup b \Leftrightarrow x \in \dagger]$
$$\Leftrightarrow \forall x[x \in b' \Rightarrow x \in a] \quad\quad \text{Det } S_{10}, S_{11}$$

13. $\forall ab[a = b \Leftrightarrow \forall x[x \in a \Leftrightarrow x \in b]]$ Th 3

14. $a \cup b = \dagger \Leftrightarrow \forall x[x \in a \cup b \Leftrightarrow x \in \dagger]$ Inst S_{13} $a \to a \cup b, b \to \dagger$

15. $a \cup b = \dagger \Leftrightarrow \forall x[x \in b' \Rightarrow x \in a]$ Bi Sub S_{14}, S_{12}

Two steps of Generalization, together with the definition of $\subseteq$, bring us to the desired statement.

5.+   1. $x \in a \lor [x \in b \lor x \in c]$
$$\Leftrightarrow [x \in a \lor x \in b] \lor x \in c \quad\quad \text{Tau}$$

2. $\forall abx[x \in a \cup b \Leftrightarrow x \in a \lor x \in b]$ Th 2d

3. $x \in a \cup b \Leftrightarrow x \in a \lor x \in b$ Inst $a \to a, b \to b, x \to x$

4. $x \in b \cup c \Leftrightarrow x \in b \lor x \in c$ Inst $a \to b, b \to c, x \to x$

5. $x \in a \cup (b \cup c) \Leftrightarrow x \in a \lor x \in b \cup c$ Inst $a \to a, b \to b \cup c,$
                                        $x \to x$

6. $x \in (a \cup b) \cup c \Leftrightarrow x \in a \cup b \lor x \in c$ Inst $a \to a \cup b, b \to c,$
                                        $x \to x$

7. $x \in a \cup (b \cup c) \Leftrightarrow x \in (a \cup b) \cup c$ Tau Inf S_1, S_3, S_4, S_5, S_6

(This technique could have been used in other proofs, but the tautology above is rather long for testing.)

8. $\forall x S_7$ Gen $\circledx a, b$

9. $\forall ab[a = b \Leftrightarrow \forall x[x \in a \Leftrightarrow x \in b]]$ Th 3

10. $a \cup (b \cup c) = (a \cup b) \cup c \Leftrightarrow$
    $\forall x[x \in a \cup (b \cup c) \Leftrightarrow x \in (a \cup b) \cup c]$ Inst $a \to a \cup (b \cup c),$
                                         $b \to (a \cup b) \cup c$

11. $a \cup (b \cup c) = (a \cup b) \cup c$ Bi Sub S_8, S_{10}

Three steps of Generalization complete the proof.

9. $\dagger = 210, \varnothing = 2$

11. (a) Only the number 3; (b) $a = 6$.

(c)

	2	6	10	14	30	42	70	210
2	2	2	2	2	2	2	2	2
6	2	6	2	2	6	6	2	6
10	2	2	10	2	10	2	10	10
14	2	2	2	14	2	14	14	14
30	2	6	10	2	30	6	10	30
42	2	6	2	14	6	42	14	42
70	2	2	10	14	10	14	70	70
210	2	6	10	14	30	42	70	210

13. (a) 2, 10, 14, 70; (b) (self-checking).

15. $1 \in e_2$, $1 \in e_4$, $-1 \in e_2$, $-1 \in e_3$.

17.

a	e_1	e_2	e_3	e_4
a'	e_2	e_1	e_4	e_3

19.

	e_1	e_2	e_3	e_4
e_1	e_1	e_2	e_3	e_4
e_2	e_2	e_2	e_2	e_2
e_3	e_3	e_2	e_3	e_2
e_4	e_4	e_2	e_2	e_4

12-2 Axioms and Definitions

1.

	1	3	5	7	15	21	35	105
1	1	3	5	7	15	21	35	105
3	3	3	15	21	15	21	105	105
5	5	15	5	35	15	105	35	105
7	7	21	35	7	105	21	35	105
15	15	15	15	105	15	105	105	105
21	21	21	105	21	105	21	105	105
35	35	105	35	35	105	105	35	105
105	105	105	105	105	105	105	105	105

3. $1 \subseteq$ all; $3 \subseteq 3, 15, 21,$ and 105; $5 \subseteq 5, 15, 35,$ and 105; $7 \subseteq 7, 21, 35,$ and 105; $15 \subseteq 15$ and 105; $21 \subseteq 21$ and 105; $35 \subseteq 35$ and 105; $105 \subseteq 105$.

5. (a) $5 \cup 21 = 105 = \mathsf{1}, 5 \cap 21 = 1 = \varnothing$.

(b)

a	1	3	5	7	15	21	35	105
a'	105	35	21	15	7	5	3	1

(c) $a' = 105 \div a.$

7. Each number can be considered as a subset of $\{3, 5, 7\}$, by identifying the number with the set of its prime factors.

9. (a) $\mathsf{1} = 1, \varnothing = 0.$

(b)

a	1	0
a'	0	1

(c) $a' = 1 - a.$

11. (a)

a	b	a'	$a \cup b$	$a \cap b$	$a' \cup b$
1	1	0	1	1	1
1	0	0	1	0	0
0	1	1	1	0	1
0	0	1	0	0	1

(b) The columns show the same pattern as the truth tables for $\sim P$, $P \vee Q$, $P \wedge Q$, and $P \Rightarrow Q$, respectively.

(c) $(a' \cup b) \cap (a \cup b')$

$$1$$
$$0$$
$$0$$
$$1$$

12-4 Moves toward Informality

There are five operators, and $2^5 = 32$.

12-5 The Duality Principle for $\{\mathsf{1}, \cap, \cup\}$

1. $\forall ac[b \cap c \subseteq a \cup b]$

3. $b \subseteq a \Leftrightarrow c \subseteq b \vee b' = \mathsf{1}$

5. $\forall a[a \neq \varnothing \Rightarrow \exists b[b \neq \mathbf{1} \wedge a' \subseteq b]]$

7. 4 and 6

9.+

1. $\forall b[a \subseteq b]$	As (Temp)
2. $a \subseteq \varnothing$	Inst $b \to \varnothing$
3. $a \subseteq \varnothing \Leftrightarrow a \cup \varnothing = \varnothing$	Th 7a, $b \to \varnothing$
4. $a \cup \varnothing = \varnothing$	Tau Inf S_2, S_3
5. $a \cup \varnothing = a$	Th 3b
6. $a = \varnothing$	Eq Sub
7. $\forall b[a \subseteq b] \Rightarrow a = \varnothing$	Ded Th
8. $\forall a[\forall b[a \subseteq b] \Rightarrow a = \varnothing]$	Gen ⓐ

11.+ Lemma A: $\exists b[a \subseteq b \wedge a \subseteq b'] \vdash a = \varnothing$

1. $\exists b[a \subseteq b \wedge a \subseteq b']$	As
2. $a \subseteq b \wedge a \subseteq b'$	Ch ⓑ
3. $a \subseteq b \cap b'$	Th 16b $a \to b$, $\quad b \to b', c \to a$
4. $a \subseteq \varnothing$	Th 3d, Eq Sub
5. $a \cup \varnothing = \varnothing$	Def $\subseteq$
6. $a = \varnothing$	Th 3b

Lemma B: $a = \varnothing \vdash \exists b[a \subseteq b \wedge a \subseteq b']$

1. $a = \varnothing$	As
2. $a \subseteq a$	Th 9
3. $a \subseteq \varnothing$	Eq Sub
4. $a \cap \varnothing = \varnothing$	Th 12b
5. $a \cap \varnothing = \varnothing \Leftrightarrow a \subseteq \varnothing'$	Th 24b $b \to \varnothing$
6. $a \subseteq \varnothing \wedge a \subseteq \varnothing'$	Tau Inf S_3, S_4, S_5
7. $\exists b[a \subseteq b \wedge a \subseteq b']$	Exam $\varnothing \to b$

By the Biconditional Theorem, $\exists b[a \subseteq b \wedge a \subseteq b'] \Leftrightarrow a = \varnothing$ is provable
We can now generalize on the variable, a.

13. This is where I get off!

INDEX